HOPE
and
HEALING

A Caregiver's Guide to Helping Young Children Affected by Trauma

KATHLEEN FITZGERALD RICE

BETSY McALISTER GROVES

Child Witness to Violence Project
Boston Medical Center

ZERO TO THREE
PRESS
WASHINGTON, D.C.

Published by

ZERO TO THREE
PRESS

ZERO TO THREE
2000 M St., NW, Suite 200
Washington, DC 20036-3307
(202) 638-1144
Toll-free orders (800) 899-4301
Fax: (202) 638-0851
Web: http://www.zerotothree.org
The mission of the ZERO TO THREE Press is to publish authoritative research, practical resources, and new ideas for those who work with and care about infants, toddlers, and their families. Books are selected for publication by an independent Editorial Board.
The views contained in this book are those of the authors and do not necessarily reflect those of ZERO TO THREE: National Center for Infants, Toddlers and Families, Inc.

Cover design: *Emily Christopher*
Text design and composition: *Schawk, Inc.*

Library of Congress Cataloging-in-Publication Data

Rice, Kathleen Fitzgerald.
    Hope and healing : a caregiver's guide to helping young children affected by trauma / Kathleen Fitzgerald Rice, Betsy McAlister Groves.
        p. cm.
    Includes bibliographical references.
    ISBN-13: 978-0-943657-93-6
  1. Psychic trauma in children—Treatment. I. Groves, Betsy McAlister.
II. Title.
    RJ506.P66R53 2005
    618.92'8521—dc22

                                                2005028188

10 9 8 7 6 5 4 3 2 1
ISBN 0-943657-93-8
Printed in the United States of America

Suggested citation: Rice, K. F., & Groves, B. M. (2005). *Hope and healing: A caregiver's guide to helping young children affected by trauma.* Washington, DC: ZERO TO THREE Press.

TABLE OF CONTENTS

ACKNOWLEDGMENTS

This publication would not have been possible without the support of the A. L. Mailman Family Foundation. We deeply appreciate their generosity.

We acknowledge the help of our local partners in the Child Witness to Violence Project: Michelle Acker, Carmen Norona, Dorcas Liriano, and Maxine Weinreb. Our national partners in the Early Trauma Treatment Network, Alicia Lieberman, Patricia Van Horn, Chandra Ghosh Ippen, Joy Osofsky, and Julie Larrieu were instrumental in the initial conceptualization of this project and provided wisdom and guidance throughout the process of writing. Charles Zeanah and Michael Scheeringa gave invaluable feedback to early drafts. We thank the wide circle of readers from across the country who gave us important feedback: Amy Bamforth, Amy Hunter, Isabella Iemma, Vanessa Peiliker, Iris Womack, Jean Youde, Lou Ann Mock, Mary Grimmer, Yvette Hyter, and Julian Ford.

Finally, we are grateful for the support of the National Child Traumatic Stress Network (NCTSN), in particular the co-directors, John Fairbank and Bob Pynoos, and the former director of the NCTSN Resource Center, Robert Franks. The NCTSN has given us steady support as well as rich resources to help us bring this project to its completion.

ABOUT THIS BOOK

Hope and Healing is an information and resource guide designed for early childhood professionals who care for children in a variety of early care and education settings. It was developed by the Child Witness to Violence Project at Boston Medical Center in collaboration with the Early Trauma Treatment Network, a national consortium of programs under the auspices of the National Child Traumatic Stress Network, and funded by the Substance Abuse & Mental Health Service Administration (SAMHSA), US Department of Health and Human Services (HHS). We wrote this book in response to questions we received from early childhood professionals from both urban and rural communities about children and trauma. Our goal in creating this guide is to give these professionals who work directly with young children affected by trauma the information they need to plan and implement successful intervention strategies for children and their families. The intervention strategies in *Hope and Healing* follow the developmentally appropriate practice guidelines for infants, toddlers, and preschoolers in group care that are outlined by the National Association of the Education of Young Children (NAEYC) and ZERO TO THREE: National Center for Infants, Toddlers, and Families.

Hope and Healing:

- Defines trauma;

- Describes trauma's effects on young children, ages birth to 5 years;

- Suggests ways in which early care and education professionals can help children and support families;

- Identifies local and national resources for professionals; and

- Offers guidance to professionals on managing the stress of working with traumatized children.

INTRODUCTION

Eric was just 4 years old that winter he was in my classroom. When he came to me, he already had a reputation in the center as "trouble." There was no question that he was "troubled." Eric lived in a household crippled by chronic violence and neglect. His mother struggled with many problems. Eric's former teacher told me that he needed residential placement. He was uncontrollable and violent in the classroom, overturning tables and smashing toys.

I was a new teacher and very nervous that first day of school. When Eric swaggered into the room with a tough guy look on his face, I thought, "Oh boy, here we go." But I was immediately struck by his vulnerability —he was just a scared child! And through some ups and downs those first few months, Eric improved. We were able to keep him in the classroom and support the family. At first I thought Eric's success was due to our diligent behavior management programs and thoughtful curriculum. Then, as children often do, Eric taught me the truth of why he was thriving.

On a beautiful snowy day, Eric lost control in the classroom and had to be moved to the time-out chair. As I struggled to calm him, Eric began crying and asking to see the snow. The window was just out of Eric's view if he sat in the chair, but if I picked him up and held him, he could gaze out at the snow-covered trees. And so there at the window we stayed, Eric calmly resting his head on my shoulder, with my arms around him. I understood then that it wasn't the time-out chair or the structured classroom program that was the key to Eric's progress— although they helped. Rather, it was the nurturing environment we had created for Eric, built on the caring relationships we had made with him that year. Those relationships of trust and care—that holding environment—are what sustained Eric and helped him progress despite the trouble at home. And when the time came for Eric to graduate to a new classroom, we were careful to help create new holding environments with new staff, a kind of chain of hands meant to guide and care for Eric as he moved forward in his life.

— K, a preschool teacher
for children with special needs

All early childhood professionals today should prepare to care for children and families affected by trauma. Young children who have been affected by trauma can be found in preschool programs, child care centers, family home child care settings, Head Start and Early Head Start classrooms, and Early Intervention programs across the United States. These children may have been exposed to community and domestic violence, war, natural disasters, accidents, or child abuse and neglect. The US Department of Health and Human Services reports that close to 1 million children a year are identified as victims of maltreatment. In addition, the National Clearinghouse of Child Abuse and Neglect estimates that between 3 and 10 million children a year witness the abuse of a parent or caregiver. The relationships that children build and the care they receive in good-quality early childhood programs can give them the strength that they need to cope with these traumatic experiences.

In recent years, therapists, educators, and researchers have learned a great deal about children, trauma, and recovery. This new information offers hope to children, families, and the early childhood professionals who care for them. Children and families can successfully manage traumatic experiences. Their recovery often depends on early childhood professionals who understand children and trauma and have the skills to help children and support families.

More than 50 years ago, pediatrician D. W. Winnicott described a baby's primary caregiving relationship as a "holding environment" (Winnicott, 2002). Winnicott believed that within her parent's arms a child develops her sense of self and an understanding of the world around her. In the years since Winnicott first wrote about the power of primary caregiving relationships, researchers have found that teachers, therapists, home visitors, and family members can also provide holding environments for young children. With the necessary training, support, and connections to resources in the community, every teacher and caregiver can give an infant or young child much of the security he needs to cope with trauma and resume his journey toward healthy development.

SECTION 1

DEFINING TRAUMA

"Hurricanes ravaged much of the Florida coast, destroying homes and knocking out power to much of the state."

CNN News Broadcast,
September, 2004

"As the van, filled with preschoolers made its way through the neighborhoods of Boston, a wounded man staggered in front of the van...he was being pursued by another man wielding a knife."

Betsy McAlister Groves,
Children Who See Too Much

"Abuse is the leading cause of death in the first year of life after the perinatal period."

National Center on Child Abuse and Neglect

" I heard a bumping noise in the night, I thought it was a monster, but it was my Dad. He was hitting my Mom."

4-year-old boy, Child Witness to Violence Project

WHAT IS TRAUMA?

Trauma is an exceptional experience in which powerful and dangerous events overwhelm a person's capacity to cope. When an adult or child is *traumatized*, they are experiencing reactions to the trauma that affect their ability to function.

It is important for early care and education professionals, parents, therapists, and others to have a common understanding of the terms "trauma" and "traumatized." More information on each component of the definition of trauma follows:

- **Trauma is an exceptional experience.** When we talk about trauma as an exceptional experience we are talking about a highly unusual occurrence, such as a severe hurricane or a shooting. Trauma is different from stress. An exceptional experience is a powerful, shocking, and extraordinary event. A severe hurricane or a shooting is highly unusual, not a typical part of life.

- **Trauma overwhelms a person's capacity to cope**. Every child and adult has some ability to cope with stress and trauma, but a child's ability is limited. One reason that children are especially vulnerable to the impact of trauma is that they have developed fewer coping strategies than adults. A child's age, developmental stage, and temperament affect that child's ability to manage overwhelming experiences. For example, a young child who is temperamentally more fearful may have a harder time coping with trauma than will a child who is older and less anxious. Children also have to rely on their caregivers' ability to help them cope. If the child's primary caregiver or other familiar adults are unavailable or unable to help the child, the child is more likely to be overwhelmed by the traumatic event(s).

Marilyn Nolt

WHAT IS THE DIFFERENCE BETWEEN ACUTE AND CHRONIC TRAUMA?

Acute trauma is a single traumatic event—such as a serious car accident—that overwhelms a child's ability to cope. Chronic trauma (also called complex trauma) means exposure to more than one—often many—traumatic events over time. Children who live in violent neighborhoods or violent homes (or both) may experience trauma repeatedly. A child who lives in an environment that exposes him to the threat of physical and sexual abuse is at great risk for chronic traumatization. Primary caregivers in these environments often cannot protect the child and his interpersonal world is in a constant state of crisis. He has no holding environment.

What Is a Traumatic Event?

- Domestic violence
- Community violence
- Terrorism, war
- Child abuse
- Natural disasters
- Life-threatening medical conditions or acute episodes of chronic illness, affecting the child, the parent, or both

For more information on these examples of traumatic events, see this guide's glossary

SECTION 2

THE IMPACT OF TRAUMA ON YOUNG CHILDREN

Until quite recently, people believed that children were not affected by trauma because they were too young to remember or understand what had happened to them. Now we have learned that exposure to traumatic events can affect all aspects of development—physical, emotional, social, psychological and cognitive—even in infants.

HOW DOES TRAUMA AFFECT YOUNG CHILDREN?

Every child who is exposed to a traumatic event will experience and respond to it in her own way (Gaensbauer, 1995; Marans & Adelman, 1997; Scheeringa & Gaensbauer, 2000).

- The type of traumatic event will affect its impact on the child.

- The child's age and developmental stage will influence how powerful and dangerous the traumatic event feels to him.

- The child's caregiving environment and social supports shape the way in which the child reacts to and copes with the traumatic event.

Risk factors and *protective factors* within children, families, and communities influence a child's reaction to traumatic events. Risk factors, such as a lack of support from neighbors or extended family, increase the chances that a powerful, dangerous experience will overwhelm the child's capacity to cope. Protective factors, such as a stable home environment, can help the child cope successfully with a traumatic experience. Risk and protective factors that are unique to a child's situation interact in complicated ways. Sometimes a single factor can be helpful and hurtful. For example, a child might be so young that he doesn't understand the full horror of a traumatic event. But the fact that he is so young means that he doesn't have coping strategies to manage the confusion and fear that overwhelm him. (More information on risk and protective factors in young children's lives can be found in Section 3 of this guide.)

William and Sasha's stories help illustrate the complex nature of trauma's impact on young children.

William, Joy-Lynn and Samuel

William (age 8), Joy-Lynn (age 4), and Samuel (5 months) were with their father in the family van when he was robbed. The father had parked the van in front of a grocery store and was just opening his door when he was pulled out of the car by a man holding a baseball bat. During the struggle, the car's windshield was shattered. The assailant ran away after he was confronted by the owners of the store, who had called the police. The father stood, stunned and injured, beside the car, with blood covering his clothes.

William was sitting in the front passenger seat and witnessed the assault. He was found by police on the street, holding onto his father's leg and crying. William had been cut on his face by flying glass. The police summoned medical assistance; William and his father were placed in an ambulance to be taken to an area hospital. Once he was placed in the ambulance, William began crying for his father. William's father did not respond, obviously disoriented by the assault.

Police found Joy-Lynn buckled into her car seat in the back of the van. Wide-eyed, she was silently sucking her thumb. It was not clear what she had seen or heard. A paramedic examined Joy-Lynn and determined that she was physically unhurt. A police officer then took her to the police station. Joy-Lynn spent several hours at the station playing with a social worker while social services tried to locate family members.

Samuel was in a rear-facing car seat next to Joy-Lynn in the back of the van. A clerk had come out of the grocery store and taken the crying Samuel out of his car seat; she was cradling him when police arrived. Paramedics found that Samuel was physically unhurt and police transported Samuel to the police station with his sister.

The father was admitted to the hospital with a concussion. He was confused and unable to identify family members who could be contacted to care for the children. William reported that he "didn't know" where his mother was and that his grandparents were dead. Social workers eventually placed William—who had been treated in the hospital emergency room for superficial cuts—and his siblings in emergency foster care.

These stories illustrate how many factors influence a child's experience of and reactions to traumatic events.

1. **A child's age and developmental stage affect the impact of trauma.** William, Joy-Lynn, and Samuel will process and understand their experience very differently because of their ages and developmental stages. For example, an infant who witnesses a beating may not understand that his caregiver has been hurt and that the red, spurting liquid is blood. An older child, however, will have a different understanding of this experience, realizing that her caregiver has been seriously injured. William will probably have the clearest memory of the trauma and a better cognitive understanding of the danger than his younger siblings. Joy-Lynn may not be able to describe clearly what happened and may be confused about details and the meaning of the event. Samuel will have no verbal memory of what happened, but may be quite distressed by the disruption in his care and familiar routines.

2. **The specific circumstances of a traumatic event help to determine its impact on a child.** Joy-Lynn and Sasha are almost the same age, but the traumas they experienced were very different. Joy-Lynn and Sasha will have their own unique

Sasha and Gramma

Shortly after Sasha's 5th birthday, faulty wiring caused a fire to break out in her family's house. When the fire started, Sasha was at home with her grandmother; Sasha's parents were both at work. The grandmother was on the second floor when she discovered smoke in the first floor hallway, blocking their escape. She grabbed Sasha, carried her to a rear bedroom, opened the window, and began screaming for help. Sasha, meanwhile, had buried her head in her grandmother's shirt and was crying for her mother. Within minutes, firefighters rescued Sasha and her grandmother through the second story window and took them to the hospital.

Sasha's parents met Sasha and her grandmother at the hospital, where both were being treated for smoke inhalation. Her parents remained with Sasha until her release 3 days later. The house was destroyed in the fire.

reactions to the traumas and show their distress in their own individual ways. Joy-Lynn may become very fearful of losing her father; Sasha may be overwhelmed by seeing a fire on television or hearing sirens in the neighborhood.

Physical injury can make the impact of a traumatic event much more serious for a child. So can being close to the traumatic event. Sitting in the passenger seat, William saw his father being hurt close up. He was injured by flying glass. Joy-Lynn may react to the trauma differently because she saw little of the assault and was uninjured physically.

3. **The child's social environment affects the impact of trauma.** The availability of primary caregivers makes a significant difference in how children respond to traumatic experiences. Strangers took William, Joy-Lynn, and Samuel and placed them in foster care. Although baby Samuel may not have experienced the assault itself as a trauma, abrupt separation from a familiar caregiver might very well have overwhelmed his capacity to cope. Sasha was able to remain with her grandmother throughout their ordeal and was quickly reunited with her parents. Sasha was comforted and supported by familiar caregivers from the very beginning of her experience.

The impact of a traumatic event is exceptionally severe if parents or primary caregivers are unavailable—physically, emotionally, or both—to support the child (Scheeringa & Gaensbauer, 2000). Unfortunately, many events, such as the severe injury or death of a parent or community violence, are traumatic for primary caregivers as well as the child. Sometimes the child's primary caregiver is also the cause of the trauma, as in child abuse. William, Joy-Lynn, and Samuel's father did not talk to or comfort his children before he was taken to the hospital, perhaps because he was injured. Social workers were unable to locate family members to care for the children; this suggested that the family had few social supports. Sasha, in contrast, was with her grandmother during the entire ordeal of the fire. Her grandmother comforted Sasha and said that firefighters would come soon. Sasha's parents arrived at the hospital soon after Sasha and her grandmother were admitted. They were constantly present and available to their daughter throughout her hospital stay.

HOW DOES TRAUMA AFFECT A CHILD'S RELATIONSHIPS AND ATTACHMENTS?

The Impact of Traumatic Events Depends On:

The Child
- Age
- Developmental stage
- Temperament
- Developmental delays
- History of emotional or behavioral problems

The Traumatic Event
- Acute trauma
- Chronic trauma
- Intensity
- Child's proximity to traumatic event
- Injury to the primary caregiver
- Loss of the primary caregiver
- Extent of physical injury to child

The Social Environment
- Availability of the parent or other primary caregiver as a support to the child
- Ability of the parent or other primary caregiver to help the child cope
- Level of family stress and coping ability prior to traumatic event
- Ability of the family to cope with current stressors
- Family routines and stability
- Availability of social supports in the community

A healthy attachment relationship is a close, connected, mutually satisfying relationship between two people. Primary attachment relationships are the relationships formed by very young children and their primary caregiver or caregivers (usually parents) in the first months and years of a child's life. The primary attachment relationship provides nurturing care to help the infant manage her physical and emotional states of hunger, distress, and fatigue.

When her needs are met, the infant is able to learn about and explore her environment. When the parent is rewarded for her efforts to care for the child with a calm and content baby, she feels capable and confident. She also learns to adapt her behavior to succeed at caregiving. This process of regulation—managing emotions and behaviors—in both parent and child is sometimes called mutual regulation or coregulation. Over time, the child begins to learn from the care she receives how to manage and regulate her own feelings and behaviors. She needs to rely less on caregivers and begins to learn to rely on her own ability to self-regulate.

In ideal conditions, the child is able to give clear signals about what he needs, and the primary caregiver is available and appropriately responsive to the child. Their social environment supports their relationship. The primary caregiver and the child begin to form what is called a secure base of attachment (Ainsworth, Blehar, Waters, & Wall, 1978) within the holding environment of the relationship.

When a child, family, or both has been traumatized, the primary caregiving relationship can be—but is not always—seriously disrupted. Many traumatized parents and caregivers manage to provide nurturing care to traumatized children. Others simply cannot. In some cases, parents who may have been closely connected to their young children are suddenly unavailable because of forced separations, injury, posttraumatic illness, or death. Ongoing stress and trauma in the family may permanently disrupt the child's attachment relationships. Parents may be the perpetrators or victims of abuse or severe neglect. The entire family system may be traumatized and unable to help the child. Yet every child needs to feel a secure base of attachment in order to explore the world and learn. Without help, traumatized children may develop cognitive, behavioral, emotional, or relationship problems.

CAN TRAUMA AFFECT THE PHYSICAL DEVELOPMENT OF THE BRAIN?

Trauma can affect the physical development of the brain (National Clearinghouse on Child Abuse and Neglect Information, 2001). Recent studies of brain development have uncovered much about how the brain grows and functions. One of the most important findings is that although genes play an important role in development, the experiences people have as young children actually drive the development of the brain. In other words, early experiences are the true "building blocks" of brain development. Scientists have also discovered that exposure to traumatic events—especially in the first years of life—can change the brain's physical development.

Janet Brown McCracken

When a young child is exposed to trauma, particularly repeated trauma, the brain and body respond in order to survive the traumatic event. The brain has to focus on survival, not learning. The body's "fight or flight" stress response turns on and changes the body's heart rate, breathing, movement, and brain function. Unfortunately, the adaptations the child develops to survive in an environment of repeated trauma may become a problem in other environments. For example, a child who is hurt repeatedly may become "hyperalert" to noises, movement, or loud voices in her environment. Her brain has learned to be "turned on" to danger at all times. The child remains in state of anxiety and may not be able to sleep or focus on learning. (For more information on brain development and trauma's impact on healthy brain growth, visit "Brain Wonders" at www.zerotothree.org)

WHAT ARE THE SIGNS OR SYMPTOMS OF BEING TRAUMATIZED?

A *traumatized child* is a child who has experienced a traumatic event and who shows signs of being overwhelmed. Traumatized children communicate their distress through their words, their behavior, and their play. Traumatized children often show behaviors that seem out of control, fearful, disruptive, or excessively aggressive. These children are *not* trying to cause trouble or "misbehave." Rather, children who experience traumatic events may become "flooded" with feelings of fear and anxiety. They cannot regulate or control these behaviors without help. Traumatic events can overwhelm a child's ability to regulate or manage the physical and emotional reactions to overwhelming experiences.

Each traumatized child will have his own unique experience of trauma and reactions to it. Some children have a severe reaction to trauma and exhibit a number of concerning behaviors. Others show fewer signs of being traumatized, but the reactions they exhibit are intense and troubling. Some children whose reactions match a specific set of behaviors and symptoms may be diagnosed with Posttraumatic Stress Disorder (PTSD). (More information on Posttraumatic Stress Disorder can be found in the glossary of this guide.)

Mental health professionals who assess and diagnose trauma reactions in children look at:

- The behavioral reactions that a child shows,

- The intensity of symptoms,

- How long the child has had the symptoms, and

- How the trauma reaction affects the child's ability to function.

Young children who are affected by trauma may show one or more of the following signs and symptoms (Lieberman & Van Horn, 2005; Sheeringa & Gaensbauer, 2000):

1. The child **relives or re-experiences the traumatic event.** The child has memories of the traumatic event playing over and over again in his head. He is flooded with memories that he can't control or stop. The child may re-enact the traumatic event through:

   - **Posttraumatic play.** Posttraumatic play is different from typical play, which feels good, helps a child express feelings, and helps a child learn. Posttraumatic play feels different to the child and looks different to adults. Children appear anxious and restricted in their play, repeating the same play patterns over and over. The play routine rarely changes. For example, a child may keep crashing two cars together, repeating the same phrase, "big boom," replaying the car accident he was in. He is not able to use the play to feel relief or mastery over the event.

   - **Preoccupation with the traumatic event.** The child may not be able to focus on anything other than the traumatic event. The child may have to play about or tell the story of the trauma over and over again—at snack time, on the playground, at circle time, and at naptime.

   - **Triggers that remind the child of the trauma.** The child may have intense, unpredictable responses to reminders of the traumatic event. Sights, sounds, smells, touch, or other reminders of the trauma may send the child into an aggressive tailspin or into a shocked state of anxiety. For example, a child may lose control at the sound of a door slamming, which brings back memories of his parents assaulting one another.

   - **Nightmares and sleep disturbances.** The child may also relive the traumatic event through nightmares about the trauma. Children can wake up screaming and begin talking about the dream that reflects the traumatic event.

2. **Hyperarousal.** The child has symptoms of anxiety, irritability, and/or impulsivity. She may have problems going to sleep and staying asleep. The body's stress response is turned on and working overtime. The child who is hyperaroused may be in a constant state of alertness to danger. She is highly anxious, unable to concentrate, and may not be able to sit still. The child startles easily, and may become fearful and clingy with changes in routine. This child always seems to be on the edge of her seat. She acts quickly and impulsively—unable to stop and think about her actions.

Sometimes adults think children who behave this way after experiencing trauma are hyperactive or have attention problems. The signs of traumatization and hyperactivity or attention disorders can look very similar. That is why it is so important for providers to learn as much as they can about every child, her home environment, and her experience. Supervisors or mental health consultants can help in figuring out what is going on with a child.

3. The child shows **withdrawn behavior, avoidant behavior, or both.** Traumatized children may try to avoid any exposure to things or people that remind them of the traumatic event. They may withdraw from activities and interactions with others, showing no pleasure in activities they once enjoyed. They may appear numb and closed off from emotions.

4. The child may exhibit **aggressive or sexualized behaviors.** All children can become aggressive when they feel frightened or unsure of a situation, but chronic aggression in young children may be a sign of exposure to trauma. Children who strike out frequently without a clear reason may be experiencing trauma in their environment. Traumatized children may also hurt animals as a way to release intolerable aggressive feelings.

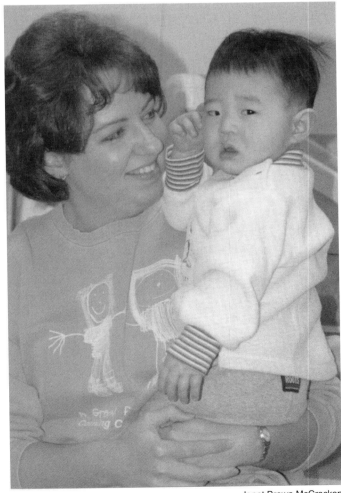

Sexualized behaviors may be a sign that a child has been abused or has witnessed overstimulating adult behavior. Some children also use sexualized behavior to relieve anxiety. Aggressive or anxious sexual behavior can be a sign that something is wrong. Adults should be concerned if a child is more anxious than curious about body exploration. Adults should also be concerned if children are acting out in sexualized aggressive ways and forcing other children to engage in sexualized behaviors, such as anxiously or aggressively pulling on or rubbing private parts.

5. **The child is fearful.** Children who have been traumatized may develop new fears or more intense fears. Fears are a common part of child

Janet Brown McCracken

Barbara Young

development, but fears that come from trauma can be overwhelming. Children who have been traumatized can be very fearful of separating from caregivers, get scared by any change in routine, and develop intense fears of specific people, places, and things.

6. The child may **regress or fall behind in development and behavior.** Traumatized children may lose developmental skills they had mastered. A child may return to "baby talk" or relapse in toilet training. Traumatized children may also withdraw from activities, appear depressed, and refuse to participate in once-favorite activities. This regression can persist over weeks or months. It interferes with learning and interactions with others.

7. The child may develop physical symptoms. Stress can cause physical illness that upsets the body's healthy balance. Traumatized children may develop headaches, stomach aches, diarrhea, or other physical illnesses. These physical symptoms are real. The child does not imagine them. Children also feel their emotions physically and may express their anxiety as a "tummy ache" or their anger as "an 'ouch' in my head."

8. The child's relationship with parents or other caregivers may suffer. In the aftermath of trauma, a child's behavior can change significantly, and a parent's ability to respond and care for her child may be impaired. Parents and children who once had a mutually satisfying, connected relationship can suddenly find themselves struggling to interact because of the distress, fears, anger, and confusion that follow a traumatic event. Parents and children who already struggle to maintain healthy relationships may find that trauma overwhelms their ability to bond and connect. Difficulties in the parent–child relationship are among the most persistent and potentially damaging impacts of trauma.

Chronic trauma may have long-term effects on child development. Exposure to chronic trauma, such as family violence, may affect cognitive and language development as well as trigger behavioral problems in children. Children cannot learn when they are highly anxious or fearful for their safety (and the safety of their parents). Traumatized children may have difficulties focusing, taking in information, and making sense of things. Children struggle to learn the puzzle of language and can have a hard time using language to make their needs and feelings known. Children exposed to chronic trauma may not learn the skills to use language as a way to manage overwhelming feelings or to communicate effectively with others. Trauma affects the brain's ability to organize, process, and store important information. Chronic trauma can damage the child's ability to learn, problem solve, communicate, and interact with the world.

Signs and Symptoms

1. Re-experiencing the traumatic event through
   - Posttraumatic play
   - Preoccupation with the traumatic event
   - Triggers that remind the child of the trauma
   - Nightmares and sleep disturbances
2. Hyperarousal
3. The child shows withdrawn behavior, avoidant behavior, or both
4. The child may exhibit sexualized or aggressive behaviors
5. The child is fearful
6. The child may regress or fall behind in development and behavior
7. The child may develop physical symptoms
8. The child's relationship with parents or other caregivers may suffer

SECTION 3

HELPING CHILDREN EXPOSED TO TRAUMA

BUILDING RESILIENCY IN YOUNG CHILDREN EXPOSED TO TRAUMA

"I dreamed my daddy ripped up my unicorn doll into lots of pieces. It was OK though, cause my unicorn still had its heart."
4-year-old witness to domestic violence

Resilience is defined as "an ability to recover from or adjust to misfortune or change" (Merriam-Webster's Dictionary, 2005). There are specific factors in children, in families, and in communities that can help children cope with stress and trauma. These characteristics in the child, the family, and community can act to protect the child from the impact of trauma.

It is important to note that these factors interact to create a dynamic process that impact on the child, the family, and the community. Characteristics in the child such as good verbal skills directly affect the way the school can help him and the way he might communicate at home. Family factors such as stability impact on a school's ability to care for a child. It is critical for early childhood professionals to see these protective factors as a dynamic system that works together to affect outcomes for children. Early care and education providers are a part of that protective system and have the power to foster coping abilities in children.

THE POWER OF CARING RELATIONSHIPS

"I was an educational supervisor at Head Start when I would get called into the preschool classroom to help. There was a 4-year-old girl in the class who would tantrum uncontrollably. She was so upset and frightened! I would have to hold on to her gently until she calmed down and could safely join the rest of the children. I felt bad—don't know how she felt about me! But years later I got the shock of my life.

Protective Factors That Support Coping and Resilience in Young Children

Child Factors
- Good cognitive ability
- Able to solve problems
- Good verbal skills
- Good self-control, able to regulate behavior
- Positively regarded personality (easy, likeable)
- Able to use adults as resources/to ask for help
- Strong self-esteem, positive beliefs about self
- Special talents or hobbies
- Has goals and the will to act on them
- Has hope for the future

Family Factors
- Presence of a stable, nurturing caregiver
- Ties to extended family
- High expectations for child
- Consistent family rules
- Well-balanced family discipline
- Family rituals, structured routines
- High parental self-esteem

Community Factors
- Safe, positive, nurturing school experiences
- Availability of supportive adults, positive role models
- Positive cultural connection, identity

Walking down the street, I heard someone call out 'Excuse me, lady!' It was a teenage girl clearing a vacant lot with a community group. 'I remember you,' she said. 'You were the lady that came and hugged me all the time at school and made me feel better.'"

Felicia, a former educational supervisor

Nurturing relationships between caring adults and children have the power to heal troubled lives. Traumatized children can benefit from a community of caring adults. Trusting, caring adults who act as caregivers and role models are a significant factor in the development of resiliency—the ability to recover from stress and trauma. Many adults who have their own traumatic histories remember teachers, coaches, grandparents, and others who believed in them and helped them to heal. Providers can be life savers to the children in their programs.

Strategies to Promote Healing Relationships Between Caregivers and Young Children in Early Childhood Programs

Two basic strategies can help infants and young children who have been traumatized to develop trust in adults and friendships with children.

Promoting Relationships Strategy #1: Create a Primary Caregiver Model of Care

Infants and young children who have been traumatized need time to develop trust and comfort with adults. Programs can create models of care that allow children to stay connected to special caregivers over time. There are many types of primary caregiver intervention models in early childhood programs that could be successful in promoting healing relationships.

1. Mixed age groups in child care give a child the chance to stay with the same caregiver over a number of years.

2. The "looping" model of teaching keeps a group of young children together with one teacher for 2 years. Children start their first year in the program with their first year teacher, then move with that teacher to the second year of the program. That teacher then "loops" back to a new first year group as her old group moves on to its third year.

3. In the special caregiver model an aide, co-teacher, or supervisor pays special attention to the needs of that child. This primary caregiver may greet the child as a ritual every morning, read him a familiar story at naptime, and in other ways be available to him in times of need. Even administrative staff can be involved as a special support to the child by establishing regular contact through visits, quiet breaks, or special time in the classroom.

Promoting Relationships Strategy #2: Help Young Children to Make Friends

Children who have been traumatized need contact and connection with peers. Friendships help children cope through difficult times. Unfortunately, making and keeping friend can be difficult for children who have been traumatized. These children may be fearful and withdrawn in group settings. They may avoid interactions with others. Children exposed to trauma may also have erratic, unpredictable, and sometimes aggressive behavior that turns other children away from them.

Children who learn the skills they need to make friends are building coping strategies to manage stress. Early care and education providers can support the development of children's social skills through:

1. **Modeling:** Caregivers can model how you ask another child to play, how you share, and how you control your body during a play activity.

2. **Direct teaching:** Children who struggle to interact with their peers may need a caregiver to play alongside them. Care providers can use class circle time to practice friendship skills with young children, read books about friendships, and problem solve with children about how to resolve conflicts with peers.

3. **The buddy system:** Older toddlers and preschoolers may benefit from being matched by caregivers in one-to-one play situations. If it seems likely that their temperament styles will work together, one child can be partnered with another during structured play activities, snack time, or outside play. These "buddies" get to know each other over time. The experience benefits both of them. A predictable play buddy may help a child who struggles to make friends learn some of the friendship skills that are hard for him to employ in a larger group situation.

CREATING SAFE ENVIRONMENTS FOR CHILDREN

"The roots of a child's ability to cope and thrive, regardless of circumstance, lie in that child's having had at least a small, safe place (an apartment? a room? a lap?) in which, in the companionship of a loving person, that child could discover that he or she was lovable and capable of loving in return. If a child finds this during the first years of life, he or she can grow up to be a competent, loving person."

Fred Rogers, *Mister Rogers Talks with Parents*

Traumatized children crave the structure of a stable environment. Exposure to trauma can make children feel out of control of their bodies, their feelings, and their safety. A structured physical environment can provide external controls that children need to begin to develop internal self-control. Children feel competent and safe when they can predict what is happening around them. These feelings of safety and security are in sharp contrast to the distress of trauma. Early childhood programs can provide the safe environment children need to begin to heal and recover from traumatic experiences.

Strategies to Create Safe Environments for Young Children

Young children who have been traumatized need individualized attention; a safe, structured environment; opportunities to talk, share, and listen; and a caring community.

Safe Environments Strategy # 1: Individualize Interactions with Children

" I knew Jess (age 2) would have her best day if I could greet her at the door in the morning with her favorite storybook Mama Loves. *We would look at it while she curled up in the cubby on top of her coat. Same thing every morning. The day wouldn't be quite the same if we missed that time together."*

Danya, a toddler teacher

Marilyn Nolt

All young children need calm and caring interactions with adults, but it is especially important to children who have been traumatized. These children may not know how to interact with adults in healthy ways. Children who have been traumatized and betrayed in relationships may not be able to control their behavior, may be fearful of adults, may not know adults as nurturing caregivers, and may test any adult who tries to connect with them.

It is important that interactions with children be individualized to meet the unique needs of each child. Thoughtfully planned interactions can function to regulate distressing and out-of-control feelings in young children. Gentle rocking, a smile, a hand on a shoulder, eye contact or any of the multitude of interactions children respond to can help them calm and get back in control. Each child is different, so the particular kind of adult interaction they need is unique to each child.

Children who have been traumatized may be fearful of touch and may not tolerate a hug but may want to sit close to a trusted teacher. An anxious infant may not like bouncing on a knee but would welcome gentle rocking. Another child may want an adult hand on his shoulder to guide him from one activity to another so he does not become overwhelmed by the transition. Some traumatized children may be terrified of loud voices and quick movements, especially during active play time. Early childhood professionals must learn each child's individual needs and adapt their own behavior in order to be helpful to children.

It is crucial for children exposed to trauma to learn over and over again that adults can be patient, tolerant, and caring, even when the child's behavior is out of control. These children may need repeated reassurance that adults can be predictably kind and clear about the boundaries of behavior in the environment. A caregiver's tone of voice, body language, and facial expressions communicate just as much to children as the caregiver's words. Caregivers have to show these children in every way that they are safe with them and valued as human beings.

It can be challenging for early childhood professionals to remain calm and patient with young children over the course of the day. Stress and fatigue are real enemies of the early childhood professional. The job calls for a significant effort on the part of caregivers to manage their own feelings, impulses, and stressors, in order to provide the nurturing care that children in trouble need. Caregivers have to recognize that frustration and fatigue are normal reactions, yet these feelings must be controlled in order to best care for the children. Caregivers who give themselves permission to breathe, count to 10, or get help from a colleague when they become overwhelmed are making healthy professional choices. (Turn to Section 5 of this book for more help on coping with work stress and fatigue.)

Safe Environments Strategy # 2: Create a Physical Space That "Speaks" to Children

"It is so amazing to watch how the children grow through the school year. They start off not knowing where to hang their coats, not sure how to find their drawing materials, acting up in the housekeeping corner. By the end of the year, they are confident and independent and know exactly where to get things to start their day!"

Kim, a preschool special needs teacher

Children feel safe and confident in physical spaces that "speak" to them. Children have their best chance to learn and succeed when the environment around them is structured to meet children's developmental needs. Environments that provide external controls—such as routines and organized play materials—help children begin to develop their own internal controls for their behavior. (See sidebar for important ingredients in creating safe spaces for children.)

A Recipe for Safe Learning Spaces for Children

1. The space is **clean and child-proofed** for exploratory play.
2. The space has **defined areas for activities** that promote all areas of a child's development—cognitive, social, physical, and emotional.
3. Each activity area is clearly **defined by its purpose.** The book area has books and chairs, the active area has mats or structures, and the art area has easels and a washable floor.
4. There is a defined **area for quiet time** with minimal stimulation from the rest of the space.
5. **Pictures and labels posted at a child's eye level** show children what to do in each activity area.
6. **Pictures and labels on toy shelves** show children where each toy can be found and returned.
7. **Rules of behavior** should be posted using simple words or pictures.
8. **A daily schedule *for children*** should be posted at a child's eye level with pictures or simple words that tell them about their day.
9. Children should have **a space of their own**—a cubby, a shoe box, a mat—that is labeled with their name and belongs just to them.

Safe Environments Strategy # 3:
Create an Open Environment for Talking, Sharing, and Listening

"Sometimes we get so busy telling kids what to do, teaching them new things, that we forget to just be quiet and listen to them."

Jeanne, preschool teacher

Children from traumatic environments are often taught "don't talk, don't feel." They learn to mistrust adults, numb themselves to feeling powerful emotions, and keep their pain a secret. Children may have been told not to talk, trust, or feel by adults in their lives. Children may also adopt these beliefs as coping strategies to survive. Early childhood professionals who model that adults can be trusted, that adults will listen, and that adults can help are giving young children just what they need.

Class Meetings, Circle Time, Listening Time

"I tell the kids—very simply—that morning meeting is a time when we can talk about our lives. I make sure everyone feels safe and everyone has a chance to speak about what is going on with them."

Kevin, a kindergarten teacher

"I see 'Circle Time' as a way to start the day with my toddlers that is predictable and comforting. They know the opening song and the good morning ritual of greeting their classmates. They also love 'talking time' when they are invited to talk about what is on their minds."

Gabe, a toddler teacher

"I make sure that all of 'my babies' get special quiet time with at least one adult caregiver every day. Every little one gets a kind of 'listening' time where we just pay full attention to the child and talk back to them about what they seem to be communicating to us. They can tell us so much just with their eyes and expressions."

Gail, an infant teacher

Traditional "listening time," "circle times," or "meeting times" in early childhood programs give children a chance to bond, talk, problem solve, and share feelings with others. Children grow to feel safer in expressing themselves when the time for sharing is structured and predictable. Early childhood professionals can encourage children to share their lives through simple games like "Show and Tell" or name games. Caregivers can act out with children how to resolve conflicts such as struggles over toys or waiting for turns. Children need to learn that their caregivers are available to them, care about their lives, and want to help. The activity may vary but the message is the same—it's OK to talk, to trust, and to feel.

Safe Environments Strategy # 4:
Build a Community of Care for Children

"My dad took me to the donut store to see my friends. Now I don't have anyone to take me to the donut store."

Michael, missing his father

Children who have been traumatized can feel very isolated and alone. They may be physically separated from familiar caregivers and uprooted from everything that they know. They may be grieving the loss of a special person in their lives. Children need connection and a sense of belonging in the world, particularly those children impacted by trauma.

School and child-care programs are natural child-centered communities. Early care and education providers can build that sense of community with their young children in large and small ways. Community-building activities with young children include relationship building, defining "community" for young children, celebrating the group as well as the individual personalities that make up the group, and connecting the school community to the larger community of neighborhood and town.

Programs can begin by teaching infants through attachment relationships that there are others in the world who will care for them. Programs can help children learn about and connect with their cultures and cultural traditions. Centers can create community in their schools with school songs and rituals. Providers can talk at circle time about how communities help each other. Children's family and culture can be celebrated through special school events. Visiting the firehouse or inviting in the local police officer to talk about community helpers are everyday activities that can help children feel connected and part of a community family.

When a Child Tells—Responding to Children's Disclosures

"A bad man tried to hurt my mommy [a police officer] last night. But she arrested him and he is in jail."

Josh, a preschooler

"My mommy and dad fight too much, I don't like that. They have a divorce, because my daddy left the house and isn't going to be my daddy anymore."

Alicia, a preschooler

Five Fun Community Building Activities for Early Childhood Programs

1. **Get creative!** Make school t-shirts, create a classroom song, develop a center motto. Have the children paint a giant "Welcome" sign for their program.
2. **Gather together as a school community.** Have regular school or child care group activities—the "all school assembly" idea. Gather as a community group for a program sing-a-long or school cheer.
3. **Celebrate community with special cultural learning days.** Families can take turns teaching the program about their culture of origin through show and tell, special snacks, or sharing songs.
4. **Plan program Family Fun Days.** Plan a school-wide picnic, field trip, or game day where children and families can interact over food, games, and sing-a-longs.
5. **Create circles of care posters.** Work with each child to create a family tree or circle of care poster. Use photos of important people in the child's life to decorate the family tree or to create the "circle of care" posters—artwork that displays photos of the child's caregivers. Display the art where children can see and interact with it.

What to Say...Responding to Children's Disclosures

1. **All children need to hear that it is OK to tell—and that their feelings are OK.**
   (e.g., "I am so glad you are telling me this! You are brave to tell your story–thank you for telling me, now I can help you!" In the story above, Alicia was upset about her parent's fighting. She needed to hear that it was OK to "not like" the fighting.)

2. **All children need comfort and reassurance.**
   (e.g., "I'll help you." "We'll figure this out." "It will be OK." In the story above, Josh needed reassurance that his mother kept herself safe—"Your Mom is so strong, she kept herself safe!")

3. **Children may need help identifying or labeling feelings.**
   (e.g., in the story above, Josh told about his mother's assault while at work. He needed help to identify and label his feelings—"Oh, was that scary?" or "That's a scary story, how did it make you feel?")

4. **Children may need help understanding the facts and that what happened was not their fault.**
   (e.g.,in the above vignette about divorce, Alicia needed help understanding what was going on—"Your daddy is still your daddy even if he doesn't live in your house. Let's talk about what divorce means.")

5. **Some conversations need to continue in private.**
   (e.g., Tia—who witnessed an assault on her mother—needed comfort and help, but a discussion in front of the other children might be too distressing—"Oh that must have been scary—let's sit at the quiet corner together and we can talk.")

6. **Some stories need immediate intervention.**
   (e.g., when a child discloses dangerous information, caregivers need to find out more about the situation and decide how to intervene. Providers could respond by saying "Tell me more about that" to gather useful information. Tia—who told of her mother's assault—may need intervention or protective services. Caregivers need to consult with supervisors or mental health consultants whenever children disclose distressing information like this story of domestic violence.)

"My mommy got a hurt last night. She had blood all over her face from my daddy."
Tia, a preschooler

These stories were told by young children during snack time at their preschool programs. The teachers overheard them but either ignored the stories or redirected the children's conversation. Those kinds of responses are understandable. Providers are caught off guard, concerned about the other children, and confused about what to say.

However, it is critically important that providers respond to children's stories in a helpful way. Children are asking for help when they tell their stories. They need to know that school is a safe place where adults want to listen and can tolerate what they have to say.

Early care and education providers have to use their best judgment to decide how to respond to sensitive disclosures, but each child does need a comforting response to their story. Some stories are too frightening to discuss with the rest of the children present. Graphic stories of violence or injury need to be contained and explored privately. Less scary stories or common experiences such as a local hurricane or fire can be explored as a group. All children—including the children that hear the disclosure—need some type of supportive response, even if the discussion needs to be continued privately. Children need to be reassured and need help sorting out the facts and feelings connected to the story. Finally, some stories may require a staff discussion about involving child protective services. (See Section 4 of this guide for more information about working with child protective services.)

Strategies to Help Young Children During Daily Activities

Caring for traumatized children does not require special activities or materials. These children need quality early childhood experiences and relationships. An early childhood professional who plans daily activities that meet the emotional and learning needs of all children, also help those who are most needy.

Daily Activities Strategy # 1: Create a Rhythm to the Day

Children and adults naturally need a balance of quiet time and active time in their day. Minds and bodies move from needing calm to craving movement and exploration. Most children and adults can read and respond to their body signals and regulate their activity level. Many traumatized children cannot. They are highly anxious, aggressive, and hyperalert or shut down and withdrawn. Caregivers can provide the external regulation—or controls—children need by structuring a rhythm into the day that responds to the child's need for calm or activity.

Morning can be a quiet time or an anxious time for a child struggling with separation. Quiet, familiar activities can be a calm way to start the morning. Afternoons in school programs can be more chaotic as infants and young children get tired and antsy after a full day of stimulation. Teachers can play active games or outdoor activities during that time. Caregivers can plan for these shifts in the group climate by having a choice of quiet and active activities that mirror the rhythms of the children.

Daily Activities Strategy # 2: Try Simple Relaxation Activities

Simple relaxation activities calm children and help them to make transitions throughout their day. The goal is to teach children to notice how their bodies are feeling and how to begin to manage their reactions to the environment.

Providers can teach children how to breathe deeply or tense and relax their muscles as a way to calm their bodies and minds. Many infants and young children calm themselves by rhythmic movement such as rocking. Some children may need more external controls to calm their bodies. Providers can try rolling those children up in blankets or encircling them with big pillows. Some children may need the structure of a story or music to begin to calm their bodies. There are many books and tapes available to help providers plan calming activities with children, but the message is a simple one. Listen to your body and use that power to calm and relax.

Simple games and exercises give children tools they can use in times of stress.

Bubble Blowing Games

Young children need to learn to notice their breathing before they can learn to control their breath. When they see what their breath can do, they begin to notice how it feels in the bodies. Simple bubble blowing games with bottles of bubbles and wands are a great way for children to begin to blow out of their mouths and take big breaths in so they can make giant bubbles!

Flower Breathing Exercise for Children

Start practicing slow breathing with children at naptime because it is a natural quiet time. Instruct children to breathe in through their noses—as if they are smelling flowers—and out slowly through their mouths. Tell children to place their hands on the bellies and breathe in feeling their bellies (or lungs) fill up like a balloon. Remind children to let their breath out slowly like a hissing snake or a gentle wind. Play quiet music with them to help them focus and relax. Practice with children regularly so they can do it during times of stress.

Daily Activities Strategy # 3: Create Smooth Transitions

Children who have been traumatized may have a very difficult time with any change in routine. Even going from one favorite activity to another can overwhelm an anxious child. Carefully planned transitions throughout the day can prevent children from feeling overwhelmed and out of control.

Tips for Smooth Transitions During the Day

Familiar child care strategies for managing transitions are especially helpful to young children who have been traumatized.

- **Let children know what will happen next**—Keep a daily schedule for kids posted at a child's eye level. Use pictures to describe each scheduled activity.
- **Give a 5 or 1 minute warning before the activity ends.**
- **Use transitional or comfort objects**—Children often transition more easily from one activity to the next if they carry an object with them. It can be a block to be used in the next activity, a book, or a favorite small toy.
- **Use poems and songs**—Barney's "clean up" song is popular for a reason! Children can go from one thing to another if a familiar song or poem bridges the gap between activities.
- **Try a relaxation exercise**—Move from a highly active activity to a table activity by calming excited bodies before you break for the table. Play a quiet song at the end of your "dance party." Have children curl up in ball and breathe quietly for 1 minute after a game of tag. Try a yoga position such as "the tree" where children are challenged to stand quiet and tall and stretch upward to the sky.

Daily Activities Strategy # 4: Make Good Toy Choices

Children can be comforted by and learn from carefully chosen toys. Toys should match a child's developmental need for exploration and mastery. They can also be used to reduce stress, express feelings, and figure out solutions to problems. Programs who care for traumatized children need to take special care that toys are in good shape, have working batteries, and have all of their parts. Children living in chaos need their early childhood programs to have "all of the pieces of the puzzle together." Organized spaces and organized toys can modulate feelings of stress and chaos for everyone.

> ### *Examples of good toy choices include the following:*
>
> **Multisensory Toys:** water, sand tables, bristle blocks
>
> **Expressive Toys:** art materials, Playdoh
>
> **Nurturing Toys:** baby dolls, blankets, bottles, multi-ethnic doll families, soft blocks, washable stuffed animals, cloth books
>
> **Protective Toys:** doctor kits, rescue vehicles, firefighter figurines
>
> **Pretend Play Toys:** puppets, doll houses, dress-up clothes, firefighter hats, doctor scrubs/gloves, magic wands
>
> **Active Toys:** beanbags, balls, swings

Daily Activities Strategy # 5:
Story Time: Use Books to Help Young Children Cope

"The right book for the right child at the right time."
Sally Driscoll, *Book Links*

Sharing books with young children can be a nurturing learning experience for any child. This experience gives them the chance to problem solve, cope, and process feelings. Story time is also a quiet escape from the stressors of daily life. Many adults remember books that were special to them and gave them positive memories. Therapists often use books on specific topics such as community violence or natural disasters to help children cope with trauma.

Books don't have to be about a specific trauma to be helpful. In fact, books that are topic-specific might be too overwhelming for young children. It is important to carefully assess what is the right book for a child at the time. Stories that are soothing, predictable, and comforting may be just right for young children. The best books for young children exposed to trauma are not just written to be "therapeutic." They are simply good quality books. Stories that address common feelings and issues related to the healing process for the traumatized child can be very helpful. For example, a child who has lost a parent to violence may respond well to a story about overcoming fears, but be overwhelmed by a stark tale of a parent's death.

Creating a nurturing environment for a frightened child with a book (such as *Goodnight Moon*) and a comfortable lap can be an important intervention for the young child. An infant may be soothed more by the rhythmic poetry of the provider's voice than the actual words being read. Another child may blossom when invited to act out the anger expressed by a story character (such as in *Where the Wild Things Are*) by stomping around the classroom. Other children may feel relieved when they learn how to conquer a fear of the dark through a story (such as *Darkness and the Butterfly*).

Should Children Be Allowed to Play With Aggressive or Scary Toys?

It is normal for young children to have fears and aggressive urges. Play is an important tool for children to learn to understand and manage these difficult feelings. Early care and education providers have to make well-balanced toy choices so that children can explore these feelings without becoming overwhelmed. Program staff need to make careful decisions about the types of aggressive or scary toys to include in their programs. Each program might have specific rules about the toys that are allowed in the classroom. Finally, each child has different developmental needs and may have fears about certain toys or play themes.

Many toys available today are too scary and too violent for children. Stores are full of frightening, realistic toy monsters with claws and bloody fangs. Toy guns look real and have shocking sound effects. There are countless evil superhero figures whose only play purpose is to kill. These toys don't help children manage scary feelings. They may do the opposite—increase a child's anxiety and aggression.

Children may really enjoy less scary toys such as an alligator toy, a plastic shark, or a cloth snake puppet to work out angry or anxious feelings. A realistic monster figurine might be too scary for children to use. Children from military families may be driven to play with soldiers and military vehicles to master scary feelings about their parents fighting in a war, but realistic toy weapons in the classroom may increase anxiety or aggressive behavior. Early care and education providers must continue to assess the balance of toys in their programs and determine whether they meet the emotional and developmental needs of each child. (Visit the National Association of the Education of Young Children's Web site at naeyc.org or call them at 202-232-8777 for more tips on making good toy choices for children.)

TRAUMATIC SEPARATIONS FROM PARENTS

A Sampler of Literacy Activities for Children

Goodnight Moon—Create a nurturing environment for an infant or child in your lap or next to you. Read the child's cues. Some traumatized children are uncomfortable with touch and may not want to sit in your lap. Share this same simple story everyday at naptime or during a transition. Create a predictable routine of book sharing that will help balance the child's chaotic and unpredictable life.

Owl Babies or *The Runaway Bunny*—Many toddlers and preschoolers love acting out these stories about separation and independence. But some children who have been traumatically separated from parents may be overwhelmed by the story themes. If the child likes the story, read it regularly so the child becomes familiar with the text. Invite the children to pretend to be baby owls waiting for their mom to return to the nest. Pretend to be bunnies hopping around the room and hiding.

Where the Wild Things Are—Max is a young boy in trouble—and angry about it. Preschoolers especially like to act out angry feelings by stomping and shouting "I'll eat you up." They may get excited by the intensity of angry feelings, just as Max does in the story. Help children regulate or manage their angry bodies by bringing them quietly back to the story with the soothing words that take Max back home in his boat where his supper is waiting for him.

When Sophie Gets Angry—Really, Really Angry—This award-winning story is beautifully illustrated with visual images of what "angry" looks like and feels like. After sharing this story with children have them draw and paint with you what angry looks like and feels like to them. Leave the activity unrestricted, don't ask children to stay in the lines! If children get too excited after a few moments or it is time to end the activity, help the children transition. In a soothing voice, show them how to calm their bodies by painting what "quiet" looks and feels like. (More information about these and other recommended books can be found in this guide's resource section.)

Children may be negatively affected by traumatic separation from their parents or other primary caregivers. These separations can be triggered by a number of circumstances. Children and parents may be separated for lengthy periods because of military deployment. Children may lose a parent permanently to death or tramatic injury. They may be removed from a parent and placed in foster care.

When a parent dies, children grieve the loss of a loved one and the loss of the world as they knew it. The grief is more complicated if a child loses a parent because of a traumatic accident, assault, or unexpected illness. Children who are separated from a parent because of child or parent illness, child protective actions, military deployment, or other stressful events can have grief reactions, too. Separations, even if they are temporary, can be very traumatic to the young child. Traumatic separations cause children to lose feelings of safety, security, and comfort.

Children grieve in different ways than adults. Sometimes, it seems as though they are not sad. A child's grief may surface at unexpected times with unexpected questions or behavior. Most children will communicate their distress through their behavior, their play, their words, or a combination of these. Children who are grieving may be more withdrawn, aggressive, moody, or clingy. They may regress in some behaviors such as talking or toileting. Caring adults need to pay close attention to what children do to communicate their grief. Fortunately, children can be guided through these difficult experiences by caring adults.

Helping Children to Cope With Loss

The following guidelines can help providers find the words and actions to help children grieve and heal.

1. **Partner with the family.** Talk and plan with the child's family whenever possible. Decide together what to tell the child and how to manage the child's reaction to the loss. Ask family members about their religious beliefs about death and loss, so those beliefs can be a part of the explanation about what happened.

2. Keep routines the same. Children feel out of control and anxious with traumatic separations.

Adults can help children feel safe and comforted by keeping the child's routines familiar and predictable. Even the simplest routines in the child's life (such as a story at bedtime) can help him feel anchored and safe.

3. Help children to feel safe. Children can feel a great loss of safety when a parent dies or when they are separated from familiar caregivers. They need to hear from trusted adults that they will be cared for and kept safe. They also need to hear that their loved one is safe (or as safe as they can be), if they are far away from them. For example:

- *"You are safe here."*

- *"I will keep you safe."*

- *"I know you miss Mommy, but your gramma takes care of her. The guards are there to keep her safe in the jail."*

- *"Daddy is with his soldier friends. They work hard to keep each other safe and Daddy is very good at keeping himself safe."*

4. Be honest. Children feel better when an adult explains what has happened in a way that they can understand. Children will make up their own versions of events, if adults don't help them understand the truth. Children can come up with very scary and destructive conclusions about what has happened (such as "Mommy left because I am bad"), so simple, honest explanations are essential. For example:

- *"Daddy had to go be a soldier. That is his job. The other soldiers will help keep him safe. He loves you and misses you and can't wait to come back and hug you."*

- *"Mommy died. Her body got hurt and it doesn't work anymore. She didn't want to leave you—she loves you very much."*

5. Keep it simple. Children need the truth about what happened, but they don't have to hear all of the shocking details of an event, especially if it will traumatize the child more. For example:

- *"Mommy has a sickness. She needs help to stop taking drugs. She can't take good care of you right now. She went to a special hospital to get some help."*

- *"Daddy got a hurt from a gun. He is getting his body fixed at the hospital. The doctors are helping him to get better."*

6. Tell children that it's not their fault. Children don't problem solve like adults do. They can come up with the wrong reasons for why things happen. They often think that they are the cause of all of the events around them. As a result, they often blame themselves when bad things happen. They need to hear over and over again that the loss event is not their fault. For example:

- *"It is not your fault that Daddy hit Mommy. Your mad words didn't make him hit me. Daddy has a problem. He had to leave the house so he can get help learning not to hit."*

7. **Expect changes in behavior.** Children will express their sadness and worry in their behavior and in their play. They may need adult help to manage overwhelming feelings that can trigger behavior problems.

8. **Help children express feelings in healthy ways.** Children need adults to model safe ways of being mad, sad, and worried. Labeling feelings, giving children things they can do to express emotions, helping children identify how their body feels when overwhelmed by strong emotions, and offering comfort are important intervention strategies.

9. **Set limits, but tolerate regression in behavior.** Children who are grieving still need to have limits for their behavior. Limits make children feel safe and in control. But children who are grieving may be too overwhelmed to control their behavior. They may regress in their behavior and return to temper tantrums or crying spells. Caregivers should be flexible in tolerating some of these behaviors. They can remind children of what the limits are, but stay flexible about enforcing them. For example:

    - *"I see you can't sit in your chair today. I know it is a hard day for you. You miss your sister and your house. Why don't you take a break from morning meeting and rest on the pillows with a book?"*

    - *"I know you have mad feelings and maybe you're scared about your mommy being far away. You can be mad, but you can't hit. Let's try punching a pillow instead."*

10. **Help children succeed.** Children can develop coping strategies to manage fears and worries. Children who can master activities or skills, and have experiences that build their confidence, can begin to feel capable of managing difficult times. Caregivers can create countless moments for the grieving child to feel "masterful and strong." For example:

    - *"I know it's hard to have Mommy in the hospital. Let's make her a picture to help her feel better."*

    - *"I notice you are so good at your ABCs. I need help making a sign for our door. Can you be in charge of making the sign?"*

    - *"Show me how good you are at yelling at those monsters in the story to GO AWAY."*

Helping Children to Cope With Loss

1. Partner with the family
2. Keep routines the same
3. Help children to feel safe
4. Be honest
5. Keep it simple
6. Tell children that it's not their fault
7. Expect changes in behavior
8. Help children express feelings in healthy ways
9. Set limits, but tolerate regression in behavior
10. Help children succeed

MANAGING CHALLENGING BEHAVIOR IN YOUNG CHILDREN

"Call them rules or call them limits, good ones, I believe, have this in common: They serve reasonable purposes; they are practical and within a child's capability; they are consistent: and they are an expression of loving concern."
Fred Rogers, *Mister Rogers Talks with Parents* (1983)

A safe, developmentally appropriate program for young children includes clear limits and boundaries for behavior. Positive rather than punitive limits give children a feeling of safety and well-being. All young children can feel out of control at times. Limits provide the external controls children need in order to develop their own internal controls (self-regulation skills) over time.

Early care and education providers need to use a firm but kind approach to children. Limits should be clear, developmentally appropriate, and consistent. A successful behavior management program will not create perfect children or perfect classrooms, but it will keep children safe, allow for healthy learning and give teachers tools to handle the challenges of childhood.

Strategies for Managing Challenging Behavior in Young Children

Four strategies can help to manage challenging behavior while promoting positive relationships. Rethinking "time out" for very young children is a worthwhile investment of time.

> ### Labels Can Help...and Hurt a Child
>
> Labeling children (difficult) or a child's behavior (challenging) can be both helpful and hurtful to the child. Labels can help a group of professionals have a common understanding of a child and her issues, but labels can have negative consequences. When professionals talk of "challenging behavior" in young children, it is important to think carefully about what they mean. Consider the following questions:
>
> ■ Does the child with the challenging behavior become a "challenging child" who is blamed for problems that are in the home or early childhood program?
>
> ■ Has the child developed a reputation as difficult because of his label—one that follows him wherever he goes? Have professionals lowered their expectations for this child and expect him to be difficult?
>
> ■ Where does the "challenge" come from? Is it the child's biology, temperament or illness? Is it family stress and dysfunction? Is the challenge from an early childhood program that does not meet the child's needs?

Managing Behavior Strategy #1:
Components of a Successful Behavior Management Program

Make sure your behavior program is comprehensive and includes all of the following important components of a successful behavior management program.

1. **Let children know what they *can* do.** Use simple words, pictures, labels and rules to explain what is OK to do. For example:

   • *Instead of saying "Stop poking him," say "Hands in your lap, not on your neighbor."*
   Instead of saying "Don't spit," say "You can spit in the toilet, not on the floor."
   Instead of saying "No throwing blocks," say "No throwing. Blocks are for building."

2. **Be flexible with the rules.** You can be both consistent and flexible with rules. If a child is under significant stress, they may not be able to comply with rules at times. There may be nonaggressive behaviors that can be tolerated under certain circumstances. Care providers can communicate what behavior is expected while at the same time communicate that they understand that what the child needs right now is a break from the rules. For example:

   • *"I know you miss your mom a lot. It's OK to lay in the book area right now. Tomorrow we'll plan for you to sit with the group at circle time."*

3. **Catch children being good.** This piece of the behavior management puzzle is sometimes forgotten in the heat of the day. It is just as important to "catch the child being good" as it is to address inappropriate behavior. Praise and positive reinforcement of desired behavior provides the balance that children need to

gain competence and confidence. Children want and need positive interactions with adults in their lives. Give them the attention they crave for the "good stuff" to help change the more challenging behaviors. For example:

• *"I noticed that you did a great job cleaning up today without any reminders! Keep up the good work!"*

4. Have an intervention plan ...or two. Providers need to employ limit-setting techniques in a carefully thought-out manner. Respond with a plan, not an impulsive reaction. Behavior management is using techniques that have been planned in advance to manage behavior. These strategies may include giving choices, planned ignoring, giving clear consequences, and then following through, or setting up a reward system for good behavior.

5. Reconnect, reconnect, reconnect! When adults and children clash over behavior, it causes a disconnection in the relationship. The adult's wishes and expectations clash with the child's abilities and desires. Children may believe the adult doesn't care for them when they interfere with the child's behavior. Reconnecting with the child after a tough interaction is essential for the child to feel safe and secure in the relationship. Reconnecting can be a kind exchange of words, a hug, a smile, or other gesture that sends a message to the child that she is still cared for and loved. For example:

• *"Boy we had a hard time together, huh? Let's shake and try again, it will be OK!"*

Managing Behavior Strategy # 2: Do Your Homework.

Gather as much information as you can on what caused the behavior, what the behavior is, and what responses have worked and not worked. You have to learn what triggered the behavior, have a clear idea of what the target behavior is and design an intervention response that addresses the cause (or trigger) of the behavior.

The Trigger + The Behavior + The Response = A Behavior Plan

A behavior plan works when providers have the information they need to create that plan. The behavior, the trigger, and the consequence are the essential ingredients that make up a behavior plan. Providers need to know what caused the behavior, have a clear idea of the behavior they want to change, and plan their response to address the cause of the behavior. Because the cause of the targeted behavior is different with each child, the responses, or consequences must be individualized for each child. It is also important for providers to remind themselves that a child's behavior is a message and aggressive behavior is often a sign of distress in the child.

Each of the stories above describes the same kind of aggressive behavior in young children—pushing. But the reasons for their behavior are very different. If a behavior plan is to be successful, providers need to design consequences to the behavior that

---

Three Children, Three Behaviors, Three Behavior Plans—Joellen, Paul, and Evan

Three-year-old **Joellen** was playing quietly in the block corner when another child ran over and plopped down next to Joellen to explore some of the blocks. The girl bumped into Joellen as she sat down. Joellen immediately pushed and kicked at the girl.

Five-year-old **Paul** came into the child-care center stomping his feet and frowning. He paused at the classroom door, looked around the room, and spotted another child sitting near the teacher. Paul walked over, grabbed the child by the shoulders, and pushed him to the ground.

Four-year-old **Evan** was fidgeting in his chair, looking to the teacher for his turn to join her at the meeting area. When his name was called, he shot out of his chair, ran towards the teacher, and plowed into another child, pushing that child to the floor.

---

address the reason for the behavior. Responding to a behavior according to a child's needs is the best way to assure a successful behavioral intervention program.

Joellen is a survivor of child abuse. She is fearful of touch and of other people. She pushed the other child in the block corner because she was surprised and scared. The teacher responded by reminding Joellen to use her words instead of pushing to tell the other girl to move. The teacher reassured both girls that they were OK and that the bumping was an accident. The teacher made a plan to discuss personal space at circle time with the group. The teacher matched the intervention to what triggered the behavior. If she had just put Joellen in time out, Joellen would not learn how to interact with others and protect her personal space.

Paul came into the classroom upset, scared, and mad. His mom was home on leave from the military and his parents had been fighting all night. He communicated his fear and confusion by striking out at another child. The teacher, after comforting the other child, spoke calmly, but firmly to Paul. "No pushing, no hurting others. You need to take a break in the quiet corner to calm your body." Paul had pushed just like Joellen did but for very different reasons. The teacher's response matched what Paul needed. He could not be a part of the group until he calmed down. Then the teacher could comfort Paul and model for him how to express himself safely.

Evan is active, impulsive, and has a hard time controlling his body. He has no history of trauma. When he pushed the child down, he did not seem to notice what happened. The caregiver responded by placing her hands on Evan's shoulders to calmly direct him back to the fallen child. "You moved too fast and crashed into your friend. Let's go back to the table and walk slowly to the meeting area. I'll help." The provider recognized that excitement and impulsivity triggered the pushing behavior. That was the behavior that needed managing. The

Managing Aggressive Behavior in Group Settings

Children who have been traumatized may have a particularly difficult time managing their behavior. These children may live in social environments that are chaotic and out of control. They are not used to limits that make sense. Children affected by trauma may also be suffering from intense emotions that prevent them from being able to balance or regulate their behavior. Children who are scared and confused can act out aggressively. Fear is often the root of aggressive behavior in children. That does not mean that children exposed to trauma cannot be cared for in group settings. Traumatized children can recover and heal with thoughtful, nurturing care.

Marilyn Nolt

teacher made a mental note to have an adult walk with Evan to the meeting area until he could go by himself. If the teacher had removed Evan from the group, he would not have learned to slow his body down.

Managing Behavior Strategy #3:
Have a Grab Bag of Behavioral Intervention Strategies

Early childhood professionals should know a variety of intervention strategies to manage challenging behavior. Each child and situation is different. This requires providers to have a range of strategies they can use comfortably and effectively.

Some favorite intervention strategies from the early childhood community include the following:

1. **Redirection.** Distract a child from the undesired behavior with something they can do. If they want to throw and reach for a block, invite them to play catch with a ball. Sometimes children need help managing their difficult feelings. Help children recognize their feelings, then try distracting children from their distress with songs, humor, or by giving them something interesting to do. For example:

   • *"I know you are sad. You miss your mom. Come, let's find your favorite book."*

2. **Choices.** Let children choose between other behaviors that are OK. This gives children a feeling of control, calms a tense struggle, and teaches children what they can do. For example:

   • *"You can look at books or pick a new toy, but you can't rip pages."*

3. **Planned ignoring.** This strategy takes thoughtfulness and care. It is best used with older toddler and preschool children who understand cause and effect.

Providers should not used planned ignoring with infants and young toddlers. They are too young to understand the cause and effect connections with planned ignoring and may feel abandoned by the adult. Staff should also remember to balance taking away attention with giving special attention to the child at other times in the day, so the child still feels connected.

Planned ignoring is when you remove all attention from the behavior that you want to stop. When you remove the attention, the child does not get what he wants and the behavior should stop. The entire staff has to be consistent in ignoring the target behavior throughout the day, or it won't work. Planned ignoring cannot be used with unsafe or aggressive behavior. For example:

- *It was time for children to pick up the toys and join the morning meeting circle. Four-year-old Josh immediately grabbed up his puzzle pieces and shouted "No!" The teacher repeated her instructions and added, "I know it's hard but it's time for meeting and I want to see you there!" Josh held firm and did not move. "When you're ready, you need to put away the puzzle and join us." The teacher went to the meeting area and ignored Josh's attempts to get her attention by stomping his feet and rolling on the floor. After several minutes, Josh put the puzzle pieces away and joined the group. He received a welcoming cheer from the teachers and children.*

4. **Teach basic problem solving.** Basic problem-solving skills are important so that children can learn to think before they act. Work through simple problem solving with children at their developmental level. Toddlers and preschoolers are still learning about cause and effect, so they need a lot of help coming up with strategies. For some children, talking about their behavior works best after "the heat of the moment" when everyone is calm. Teachers have to use language and problem-solving strategies that are within the child's abilities to understand. For example:

   - *"I know you want to color too, but you can't grab crayons from others. What else could you try to get crayons?"*

   - *"Remember at choice time when you ripped up your art work? Let's figure out how to deal with your mad feelings when you get frustrated, without hurting something."*

5. **Simple reward systems.** Young children need to be rewarded for appropriate behavior as soon as they behave successfully. Delayed praise or token systems that expect a young child to earn points toward a prize over a period of days don't work for toddlers and preschoolers. It is very hard for children to wait for a sticker at the

---

Tips for Time Out/Break Time

1. **The time out (or break) area should be comfortable and feel safe.**
2. **Make it positive.** Teach children that there is a safe place in the room that they can go to calm down or get in control. They may be less resistant to time out if it is presented in a positive way.
3. **Be clear about the rules and boundaries of break time.** Some children feel less anxious about sitting away from the group if there is a timer that sets a clear beginning and end to the break time. Some children grow to welcome their break time and will tell you when they are calm enough to rejoin the group.
4. **Infants and toddlers should not be expected to sit in a time-out chair.** Older children should only be expected to stay in time out for no more than 1 minute for each year of life (e.g., 3 minutes for a 3-year-old, 5 minutes for a 5-year-old), unless they want the extra time to calm.
5. **Provide structure.** Some children may need the structure of a chair, pillows, or a mat that defines the break area. Some children need a provider close by—one who monitors the child but does not give extra attention to any negative behavior that the provider is trying to stop.
6. **Reconnect.** When the child returns to the group, make a point to welcome him with kindness.

Stories of "Time Out"

Joseph has hit another child after being warned to stop and reminded to use his words to communicate. The provider calmly but firmly tells Joseph he will need to go to the break area until he calms down. In the break area, Joseph yells and bangs his chair. The provider stands near by with her back to Joseph, reminding him that when he sits quietly, he can return to the group. Joseph then runs towards the snack area. Without making eye contact or saying anything, the provider guides Joseph back to the chair and reminds him that when he has calmed down, he can return to the group. After another attempt to leave the area, Joseph sits quietly for a minute or two. The provider joins him, gives him the hug he seeks, and talks to him about keeping his hands to himself. Both rejoin the group.

Carmen is a young toddler who is very active and physical. During a play session with building toys, she reaches out and slaps her teacher. The teacher reminds her that there is no hitting and to use her words if she wants to say something. Carmen slaps her again. The teacher gives her a firm "no" and moves out of Carmen's reach, turning her back to Carmen. After a moment, Carmen says "No hitting" and the teacher rejoins her with a hug and a smile. The hitting has stopped for now, and Carmen is learning boundaries for her behavior.

A creative preschool teacher has turned her time out area into "Australia." She has read the book *Alexander and the Terrible, Horrible, No Good, Very Bad Day* to her class. She reads to the children that Alexander gets so angry and upset one day that he yells at his mother and hits his brother. Alexander is so frustrated that he wishes to go far away—to Australia. The teacher tells the children that everyone has bad days and everyone has to learn to calm themselves. She introduces the time-out area as "Australia"—a place to go to calm down, get a break, and think about things. The teacher takes time to set up some rules about Australia, plans for when everyone decides they want to be there, and works out with the children the best way to manage the break time.

end of the day and they often forget the connection between the behavior and the reward. Children also need to understand cause and effect—and young children are just beginning to understand connections between events.

Rewards should happen quickly and they also should be something the child wants. Most children just want adult attention. Some older toddlers and preschoolers may love getting a sticker at the end of an activity. Other children may work to be chosen as the teacher's special helper (as long as everyone gets a turn!). Find out what works for each child. But remember to balance out issues of fairness that will come up with older children. As one wise teacher told her students, "Everyone gets what they need in my class, but everyone needs different things." For example:

• *"Let's see who is using their eyes and ears to listen and look—they can be Snack Helper today."*

• *"Look at you! You have had a 5-star day! You earned a star for every activity!*

6. Time out. Time out means different things to different people. It can be an effective strategy for children who need help controlling their aggressive behavior. It can also be easily misused and abused, making difficult situations worse.

Managing Behavior Strategy # 4: Rethink Time Out

Head Start has written about time out and how it should be used. Head Start states that time out means removing attention for an undesired behavior. It does not mean punishing a child. Removing attention does not mean that the child needs to sit in a corner. It can happen by moving a child a few feet back from a group activity while he settles down or by having an adult move or turn away from the child in response to negative behavior. Head Start emphasizes that time-out techniques need to be a part of a well-planned behavior program that uses a range of strategies that emphasize positive reinforcement and nurturing interactions.

In order for time out to be successful, it needs to be used in a positive way. Time out can be thought of as "break time." It is a time for a child to get a needed break from what has become a stressful time. When a child struggles with out-of-control or aggressive behavior, he needs external controls to help him calm down and feel better. Time out from the group can be a great way to help a provider help a child regulate his behavior. Children who lose control because they are highly anxious or aroused may truly benefit from a break in a comfortable, quiet, welcoming part of the classroom.

When a Child Needs More—Safety Concerns in Group Settings

There are some children who have such aggressive behavior that safety is a concern. Some children may need a more intensive intervention program than the community preschool program or child care center that they are in. It is a difficult decision to remove a child from a program. That decision should never be made impulsively or out of fear or frustration. Any decision to remove a child from care out of concern for the safety of that child or others needs to be carefully considered by the entire care team. The care team should include any providers, supervisors, directors, and mental health staff that work with the child. Parents should be included whenever possible in the decision-making process.

Early childhood professionals should seek mental health consultation from programs in their area for these difficult decisions. There are no clear guidelines to follow in making a decision about a child's placement because each child and program are unique. But before a child is removed from a program, staff should be able to say that they did everything in their power to make the best choice for that child and their program. And finally, any decision to remove a child from a program should include a plan for telling the child—and the other children—in a way that discourages them from feeling blamed, abandoned, or anxious.

SECTION 4

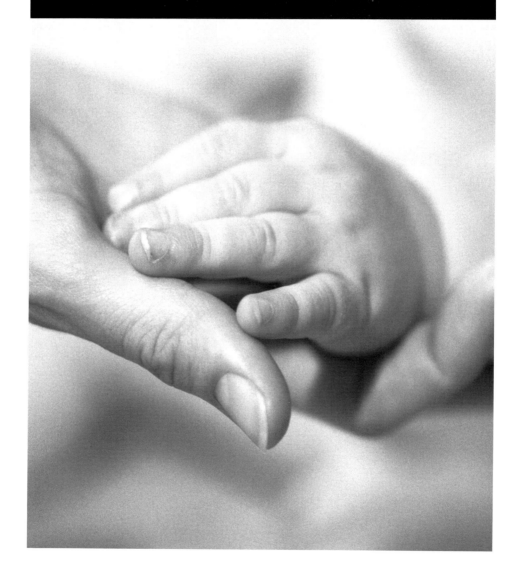

SUPPORTING FAMILIES AFFECTED BY TRAUMA

"In spite of the six thousand manuals on child raising in the bookstores, child raising is still a dark continent and no one really knows anything. You just need a lot of love and luck—and, of course, courage."

Bill Cosby, *Fatherhood*

BUILDING PROFESSIONAL RELATIONSHIPS WITH FAMILIES

A working relationship between parents (or other family caregivers) and early childhood professionals is necessary in order to help children. Respectful relationships with parents are always important, and they are critical if a crisis hits the family. It may be a challenge to connect with busy, stressed, or troubled families, but it is a challenge that the early childhood community needs to meet head on.

Early childhood professionals report many real barriers to making relationships with families. Parents are busy and struggling to balance work and home responsibilities. There may be language and cultural differences between parents and providers that challenge the relationship. Parents may be nervous about sharing family information because they do not want to be judged by professional caregivers. Families may be difficult to connect with because they are traumatized and struggling to cope. Finally, some families may not be willing to communicate openly because they are involved in inappropriate or illegal activity.

Early care and education providers may have strong feelings about parents when they believe a child is being neglected or mistreated. These feelings are understandable, but they can be barriers to working with families. Providers need to manage feelings of anger and frustration at parents, so they can continue to strive for a connection. It may be difficult for providers to take on the primary role of reaching out—and continuing to reach out to families—but it is in the child's best interest to keep trying. Parents and providers who have good working relationships model for children how healthy relationships work. (See Section 5 of this booklet for ideas on managing difficult feelings and job-related stress.)

Essential Steps in Strengthening Relationships With Parents/Family Caregivers

1. **Reach out to families at intake.** Begin the process of connecting with families as soon as the child enters the program. Let parents know that your program believes in working partnerships with families. Create or share your program's philosophy of parent involvement. Consider making a home visit as a part of the program's intake process.

2. **Find common ground.** People make relationships together when they connect over common interests and desires. Providers and parents, no matter how different, have the care and concern for the child in common.

3. **Walk the walk.** Family-focused care is easy to talk about but hard to do. Take concrete steps to involve even the busiest families in your program. Print your program's philosophy of parent involvement in the parent handbook. Post a parent information bulletin board. Give families choices of ways they can be involved in the program in large and small ways.

4. **Be creative with communication.** Programs can communicate with parents in a number of ways—phone calls, email, newsletters, parent–teacher meetings, home visits, pot-luck dinners. The choices are endless, but they need to reflect the communication styles of the families in the program. Remember, some parents may be struggling with limited literacy skills or language barriers.

5. **It is up to you.** Programs have to take the lead in connecting with families. Families can be wary or shy about program involvement. Even if families don't write notes or call, providers should continue to reach out to them. That next phone call may be the one that brings parents and providers together.

6. **Manage difficult feelings.** Negative feelings about parents are barriers to making relationships. Get help with managing these feelings in supervision (if you have it) or from respected peers so you can maintain a professional tone with parents.

7. **Be generous with your empathy and respect.** People thrive in relationships where they are respected and feel that someone else understands them. Strive to maintain a respectful tone with parents and take a moment to walk in their shoes. Empathy and understanding go along way in building good working relationships.

TALKING ABOUT SENSITIVE ISSUES WITH FAMILIES

It can be stressful for early childhood professionals to talk with parents about sensitive issues. Under the best circumstances, parents and providers have a trusting working relationship and share each other's concerns. At other times, parents and providers may disagree or may not know each other well. The conversation can become more challenging. In either case, planning and preparation are critical to a successful intervention with families. The following guidelines will help you prepare to talk with parents about sensitive issues.

1. **Have a plan.** Discuss with your team or supervisor how you will talk with parents. Which staff member should take the lead in the discussion? Where will you meet? What will you say?

2. **Think of it as a conversation, not a confrontation.** Don't assume the worst. Keep a positive attitude going into the meeting and keep the tone positive.

3. **Rehearse and role play.** Practice what you will say and how you will say it. Ask a colleague to role play with you. Figure out what words sound the least threatening and most empathic.

4. **Begin with the positive.** Always begin a conversation with positive news or comments about the child. It breaks the ice and may help a parent feel more comfortable.

5. **State the goals of the meeting.** Be clear from the beginning why you are meeting. State a few simple goals that you hope are achieved in the meeting. Ask parents what their goals are.

6. **Stick to the facts and avoid judgment.** State observations of the child or facts you have gathered to explain your concerns. Avoid making judgments about what you *think* is happening. For example:

   • "I'm worried about Jackie's behavior because I observed her doing…" rather than a less clear "There is something wrong with Jackie." Try saying "William said that there was nothing to eat at home and often eats several large bowls of cereal," rather than "I don't think you are feeding this child."

7. **Use active listening.** Show parents respect by actively listening to what they have to say. Make eye contact when appropriate, lean toward parents if it is comfortable. Repeat back to them what you heard them say so that you are both clear about the conversation. They will feel respected and heard.

8. **Create a plan together.** Develop a concrete "To Do" list about what will happen next. If parents and early childhood staff agree on a plan, that is great. Parents and caregivers may also agree to disagree. Early childhood staff should keep the lines of communication open as next steps unfold.

9. **Summarize.** Thank parents for coming. Review the discussion and summarize key issues and goals. State follow-up plans clearly.

10. **End with hope.** What can you say that will offer an honest, hopeful message? Hope carries people through even the toughest times. Make a hopeful comment part of every meeting. Anxious parents really need to hear that you believe that progress is possible!

WORKING WITH OTHER AGENCIES INVOLVED WITH THE CHILD AND FAMILY

Early childhood professionals who strive to work together with the other agencies in a child's life have the best chance of working successfully with both child and family. Important guidelines for working with other agencies are presented here.

Strategies for Successful Work With Families Involved With Other Agencies

Well-informed early childhood professionals can help to connect families with respected community agencies and help to coordinate family services.

Working With Other Agencies Strategy #1: Collaborate With Agencies to Support Families

Collaborating—working together toward the same goals—is an important intervention strategy for the early childhood professional. Agencies that communicate with each other and work together to provide family services have the most successful models of care. Children who have been traumatized, particularly those exposed to chronic trauma, may be involved with a number of agencies and programs.

In the best cases, there is one agency or professional who functions as a "case manager" for the family and helps coordinate services. Unfortunately, many families do not have coordinated services or a case manager. A number of agencies may be working with one family, but don't even know the other agencies are involved! This can create confusion, stress, and poorly delivered services to families. It is especially important that professionals work together when they are caring for traumatized families. Otherwise, agencies are at risk of creating further chaos, disruption, and mistrust within the family system.

Early childhood programs can begin the collaboration process with other agencies as part of the program intake process. Families can be asked to list contact information for the other agencies involved with the family. Programs can ask families to sign releases in order for programs and agencies to talk to each other. Early childhood programs can keep files on family information and agency involvement. Some parents may be reluctant or refuse to sign releases to other agencies, even after hearing the benefits of open communication. As long as the legal system has not altered parental rights, parents do have that right to refuse communication between agencies.

Working With Other Agencies Strategy #2: Connecting Families With Resources

When a child has been traumatized, family members may be so overwhelmed that they are unable to access the help their child needs. As a primary contact or support person, it often falls to a teacher or other caregiver to help families find therapeutic services. The positive, trusting relationships formed between care providers and families can be the springboard for even the most reluctant families to get help for their child. When early care and education providers know the services available in the community, they can help children and families in trouble. One of the most important resources an early care and education program can have is mental health consultation from community mental health programs.

Tips for Finding Local Resources for Families

Finding appropriate and responsive local resources takes knowledge, perseverance, and an ability to establish and maintain good relationships with other professionals.

1. **Know the "big four" of community resources.** Every early care and education program should know about and have contact information for the four essential community service programs:

   - the local hospital/health clinic
   - local/state child protective services
   - local mental health clinics/programs
   - the community school system (early intervention, special education services, public schools).

   Other community agencies include law enforcement and the legal system.

2. **Create a resource guide.** Be prepared before a crisis hits. Include agency names, program descriptions, contact people, and phone numbers. Keep numbers and contact people updated yearly. Brainstorm with staff about what to include in your resource guide. You can include information about counseling services, health care, housing, job training, parenting programs, libraries, food pantries, recreational programs, and more.

3. **Designate.** Assign (or ask for volunteers) a staff person or persons to organize the resource guide. Choose someone who is comfortable talking on the phone or in person. Give staff time in the schedule to keep the resource guide up-to-date and comprehensive.

4. **Remember confidentiality.** You can talk to other agencies about your program needs and children, but you cannot use family or child names without permission.

5. **Ask trusted professionals.** Ask experienced professionals in you program or community what services they would recommend. Trusted professionals could be social workers, doctors, nurses, and other teachers.

6. **Use local government services.** Town hall, city hall, and state child and family service agencies can help you find out about what is available in your community for families and children.

Barara Young

7. **Create a professional network.** Get to know your local health care clinics, family service programs, schools, and mental health programs. Call and ask for written information about the services they provide. Offer to send information about your program to them.

8. **Check everything out.** Ask questions. Good agencies should welcome questions, not avoid them. Are the agency and staff licensed and experienced? What kind of reputation does this agency have in the community? What do other families think of these services?

What Is Mental Health Consultation?

Mental health consultation is when an early care or education program has licensed mental health therapists available to help program staff. These mental health clinicians are available to talk about issues that come up with children and families. Sometimes mental health consultants attend program staff meetings, provide trainings to staff, do child and family assessments and/or provide therapeutic services to families and children enrolled in the early childhood program. Sometimes mental health consultants are available in an emergency to help manage crises that may occur.

Early care and education providers who do not have a mental health consultant connected to their program can try to set up those services. Providers can ask their supervisors for help, call local community mental health agencies, or ask the medical doctor or clinic connected to the early childhood program for help. (See the tips on finding resources for more information on getting the help that providers—and families—need.)

REPORTING TO CHILD PROTECTIVE SERVICES

Laws in all states designate early childhood professionals as "mandated reporters." This means that early childhood professionals are required by law to report suspected child abuse and neglect. The decision to make a formal complaint of child abuse or neglect may be the most complicated decision faced by the early childhood provider.

Guidelines for Reporting Child Abuse and/or Neglect

Although there are no easy answers, the following nine important guidelines can help early childhood professionals create an intervention plan that works.

1. **Be informed.** Know your state laws and program policies. Every licensed child care or education program should have a clear policy on child abuse and neglect issues. Those policies tell you what to report and how.

2. **Ask for training.** Most states are required to train mandated reporters on issues of child abuse and neglect. Your state child protective agency should be able to come to your program and train staff. Insist on help from your state agency that handles child abuse and neglect cases.

3. **Contact the National Clearinghouse on Child Abuse and Neglect** at 800–394–3366 or on the Web at www.nccanch.acf.hhs.gov for information on child abuse and neglect.

4. **If you can, don't go it alone.** A decision to file a report of child abuse or neglect should be made by the team (supervisor, director, mental health consultant) whenever possible, not by just one person. There should be a team discussion of the situation and a team intervention plan.

5. **Keep careful notes.** Write down what you observe that concerns you. Is it the way the child plays in the doll corner? Is it his toileting behavior? What exactly is happening? Remember to stick with facts. Write down what you see, not what you think is happening. The notes will help your team make decisions.

6. **Don't jump to conclusions.** Just because you see something that worries you, this doesn't mean you know what happened and who did it. Stick with what you see, not what you imagine is going on.

7. **If a child's play worries you, ask him to tell you more about it.** More information may help your team decide what to do. Ask children open-ended questions like "What happened?" "What did you see?" or "Tell me more about that…" that invite a description of the event, not leading questions like "Your dad hit you, didn't he?" which may get a confused "yes/no" answer.

8. **Decide who will make the report.** If the team decides to call in a report, choose who will make the call. If there is a concern that the parent–provider relationship might be damaged, the director may want to file the report. The teacher can then try to maintain a relationship with the family, as long as the family knows that the program staff is united behind the decision to file. The staff person who makes the report needs to be in charge of follow up and keep track of all the paperwork and plans that follow.

9. **Whenever possible, inform the family before you file,** but remember, each case is unique. Staff must carefully discuss the best option for the family, the child, the staff, and the relationship they have together. Staff must also decide who should inform the parents and how best to tell them. If possible, the family should be invited to be a part of the process from the beginning. They can be present in the room when making the call or be invited to make the call themselves.

SECTION 5

ON THE JOB: STRESS AND COPING FOR THE EARLY CHILDHOOD PROFESSIONAL

"The single most important factor in the success or failure of trauma work is the attention paid to the experience and needs of the helper."

Saakvitne & Pearlman, *Risking Connection*

Working with young children can be fun, rewarding, and fulfilling. It can also be challenging, frustrating, and exhausting. Caring for and teaching young children is one of the most important jobs in the world, yet early childhood professionals are often underpaid, undervalued, and overworked. In addition, early childhood professionals are caring for more and more very needy young children. These professionals may not get the training and support they need to provide the special care that these children require.

Working with traumatized children can be very difficult for even the most gifted and caring professionals. Exposure to the tragic stories of children can shake a caregiver's views and beliefs about the world and the people in it. The traumatic experience faced by the child can trigger the same feelings of fear, anxiety, and hopelessness in the caregiver that the child is feeling. Exposure to traumatic stories can bring up long-buried emotions or memories from the caregiver's childhood.

These reactions to the work are very normal, but they can also be crippling. It is very important that early care and education providers take care of their own health and well-being, so they can thrive as individuals and as professionals.

THE SPECIAL STRESS OF WORKING WITH TRAUMATIZED CHILDREN AND FAMILIES

Most early childhood professionals would say "you know burnout when you feel it." Feelings of stress, exhaustion, and sadness are common feelings among providers who work with needy children. Burnout is a very real and debilitating state that affects job performance and health. Burnout is the psychological strain of working with challenging populations. Early childhood professionals describe feelings of frustration, anger, and sadness. They feel exhausted and complain of headaches, stomach upset, and muscle aches and pains. These negative feelings persist over time. Professionals who feel burned out just don't look forward to going to work on most days.

"After working with young children in a domestic violence shelter for a few years, I really became affected by the work. All of these violent stories played in my head at night and I began to feel very unsafe going through my daily routines. I think I was seeing the world in a whole new way. It seemed more violent and scary."

K, a child advocate

Early childhood professionals who work with traumatized children are exposed to unique and intense stressors that can have a strong impact on the caregiver's physical and emotional well-being. These reactions to the work may be more than burnout. Experts have discovered that caregivers who work with traumatized children can develop conditions called "secondary trauma" or "vicarious traumatization" (Saakvitne & Pearlman, 1996).

These conditions reflect the very challenging role caregivers have when they bear witness to child trauma. Many caregivers describe feeling a kind of secondary trauma—experiencing some of the same symptoms of trauma that the child is exhibiting such as anxiety or nightmares. Other caregivers describe feeling exhausted and hopeless. Still other caregivers describe being deeply and profoundly changed by working so closely with trauma victims. Their inner view of the world and the people in it becomes disrupted and sometimes troubled. They feel helpless and hopeless.

This deep transformation of the caregiver's inner experience is a primary condition of vicarious traumatization. Caregivers begin to feel that their beliefs in the world are shaken and they see things in a troubling new way. Vicarious traumatization in the caregiver occurs when the caregiver has trouble coping with the story of the trauma, just as the child has trouble coping with the trauma experience.

Working with traumatized children can be especially difficult for caregivers who have their own traumatic life histories. These caregivers may be the most empathic and helpful to children because they can really understand what the child is going through. However, they can also be at the greatest risk for vicarious traumatization themselves if they lack the coping strategies and support to manage their reactions. For example, a caregiver who is called to comfort a child who has lost her father in an accident may be overwhelmed with old memories and feelings about the sudden loss of her father at a young age. These feelings may be very difficult to manage. Caregivers who are closely connected to young children may be overwhelmed with feelings of sadness, anger, anxiety and helplessness.

HOW CAN I TAKE CARE OF MYSELF AS A PROFESSIONAL?

Fortunately, there are many ways that caregivers can support and nurture themselves as professionals caring for young children. The first step is recognizing that the best way providers can care for children is to keep themselves mentally and physically healthy. Caregivers who are used to caring for everyone else except themselves may have a hard time rethinking their behavior. If providers prioritize self-care, they are giving two gifts—one to themselves and one to the children in their care.

Strategies for Self-Care

Effective self-care includes stress management, peer support, and high-quality on-the-job supervision.

Self-Care Strategy #1: Stress Management

Bodies respond to stress in physical and emotional ways. When the mind sees a threat in the environment, it triggers chemical reactions in the body that prepare it to deal with the stress. Bodies have a "flight or fight response" to the stress in the environment. The brain tells the body to breathe faster, tense muscles, and get ready to run or defend itself. Unfortunately, if the mind feels attacked repeatedly, it is triggering the body's stress response over and over again. This is the "wear and tear" of chronic stress—bodies in a chronic state of arousal without relief.

Studies have shown that chronic stress is related to physical illness such as headaches, stomach problems, back aches, and even heart disease. Fortunately, the mind is able to calm the stress response just as the mind can trigger it. The body can release chemicals that counteract the stress response and return the body to a relaxed state. Simple rules of self-care help the body trigger calming responses and help the mind cope with daily stress.

Self-Care Strategy #2: Peer Support

Positive connections with coworkers and support from colleagues can offer healthy protection from job stress and trauma. Many early childhood professionals say that no one understands the stress of working with young children better than other teachers. Trusted peers and coworkers can listen and empathize without judging. Peers can provide solutions to problems and relief from the feelings of isolation that can occur.

Creating a Climate of Respect

Administrators and other staff can combat burnout and stress by creating a climate of respect among program staff. Professionals who treat each other with respect and care model for children how healthy relationships work. Simple practices such as saying hello and good-bye, complimenting hard work, and listening to coworkers in need, can set a positive professional tone in a program. Staff should have the time to communicate regularly and have a safe place to talk about difficult interpersonal issues. It is critical that the administrators, supervisors, and staff model the kinds of relationships they wish to promote among families and children.

Mentoring Programs

Peer support often happens without planning but can also be carefully nurtured by program staff and administration. Mentoring programs where experienced and novice staff are paired together can be effective peer support programs. Peer support groups that meet over lunch or after work hours can also be strong remedies for job stress.

Ten Tips for Self-Care for the Early Childhood Professional

1. **Eat well.** Don't skip meals, especially breakfast. Reach for healthy foods during that late afternoon slump. Avoid sugar, caffeine, and junk food because they only give you a temporary boost of energy. These foods also cause an energy "crash" only a little while after eating them, when the sugar or caffeine is processed in the body.

2. **Drink fluids.** Drink plenty of water or other noncaffeinated drinks during the day. Dehydration can cause fatigue and other ailments.

3. **Exercise.** Regular exercise is a great stress reducer. Walking, yoga, basketball, or any other activity that gets the body moving triggers the release of calming chemicals that fight stress.

4. **Sleep.** Make sure you get the sleep you need. Create a quiet routine at bed time to help you fall asleep. Try a bath, music, or reading. Turn off the stressful night time news shows. Catching up on lost sleep does help. Imagine you have a sleep "bank." If you lose sleep, try to catch up with a nap so you keep your sleep bank full.

5. **Laugh.** Laughter really is the best medicine. Studies have shown that regular laughter actually helps the body heal from illness! Find the funny in daily life or seek out comedies at the movie theater.

6. **Discover your passion.** What do you love to do? When was the last time you did it? Crafts, reading, music, dance—remember or discover what lights a fire in you. Passions renew our spirits and gives us breaks from daily stress.

7. **Relax.** Schedule quiet time in your daily routine, even if it is only 5 minutes. Listen to soothing music, pray, or practice relaxation breathing. Just 5 minutes of daily meditation or quiet breathing has been shown to improve health.

8. **Balance.** Strive to create balance between work, play, and rest in your life. Learn to say no to tasks that create a work overload. Build in a walk or a bath into a day of hard emotional work. Let the laundry pile up so you can see that movie!

9. **Treat yourself.** Do something that is just for you! Cook your favorite meal. Wrap yourself in a blanket and listen to your favorite music. Think of a treat or activity that is just for you to enjoy and do it!

10. **Connect.** Friends can be the best remedy for a stressful work life. Take time to connect with friends, family, and coworkers who give you an emotional boost and fill you with good energy that will carry you through a tough day.

Self-Care Strategy #3: On-the-Job Supervision

"I didn't know what was missing until I had it. I did not have any supervision at my last job. I have it with this teaching position. Supervision has allowed me to grow as a professional and cope with the stress of working with very challenging kids."

M, a preschool teacher

An essential—and often missing—component of quality early childhood programs is staff supervision that meets the unique needs of professionals working with traumatized children and families. Clinical supervision is almost always provided to mental health clinicians working with troubled families. Professionals in education are only beginning to see the importance of quality supervision in the early care and education field.

Experts agree that quality supervision contains important components. First, effective models of supervision are process-oriented. Process-oriented models allow the caregiver to reflect on her feelings and reactions related to the work in a safe environment. Process-oriented supervision focuses on processing the experiences of the caregiver, not on instructing the caregiver. The caregiver grows as a professional and copes with difficult feelings by talking, sharing, and reflecting with her supervisor. Supervisors use the caregiver's experiences as teaching tools. They help caregivers discover solutions to problems, rather than just giving information and telling them what to do. These models of supervision also require that the supervision experience be safe, confidential, and supported by program administration.

High Quality Educational Supervision Is:

- Facilitated by an experienced professional
- Safe and confidential
- Process-oriented—focused on self-reflection as a teaching tool, not on instruction
- Supported by the administration—Care givers are given the time and space for supervision

For more information on models of effective process-oriented supervision, see *Learning Through Supervision and Mentorship: A Source Book*, edited by Emily Fenichel (1992).

"Those of us who are in this world to educate—to care for—young children have a special calling: a calling that has very little to do with the collection of expensive possessions but has a lot to do with the worth inside of heads and hearts. In fact, that's our domain: the heads and hearts of the next generation, the thoughts and feelings of the future."
Fred M. Rogers, *Young Children*

Marilyn Nolt

REFERENCES

Ainsworth, M., Blehar, M. C., Waters, E., & Wall, S. (1978). *Patterns of attachment: A psychological study of the strange situation.* Hillsdale, NJ: Erlbaum.

Cosby, B. (1987). *Fatherhood.* New York: Berkeley Trade.

Driscoll, S. (1999). Coping with violence. *Book Links, 9*(1) Available at http://www.ala.org/ala/booklinksbucket/copingviolence.htm

Fenichel, E. (Ed.) (1992), *Learning through supervision and mentorship: A source book.* Washington, DC: ZERO TO THREE.

Gaensbauer, T. (1995). Trauma in the preverbal period: Symptoms, memories, and developmental impact. In A. J. Solnit, P. B. Neubauer, S. Abrams, & A. S. Dowling (Eds.), *The psychoanalytic study of the child* (pp. 122–149). New Haven, CT: Yale University Press.

Groves, B. (2002). *When children see too much: Lessons from the child witness to violence project.* Boston: Beacon Press.

Lieberman, A., & Van Horn, P. (2005). *Don't hit my mommy!: A manual for child–parent psychotherapy with young witnesses of family violence.* Washington, DC: ZERO TO THREE Press.

Marans, S., & Adelman, A. (1997). Experiencing violence in a developmental context. In J. Osofsky (Ed), *Children in a violent society* (pp. 202–222). New York: Guilford Press.

Merriam Webster's Collegiate Dictionary (11th ed.). (2003). Springfield, MA: Merriam Webster Publishing.

National Clearinghouse on Child Abuse and Neglect Information. (2001). *Understanding the effects of maltreatment on early brain development.* Washington, DC: Author.

Rogers, F. (1993). *Mr. Rogers talks to parents.* Pittsburgh, PA: Family Communications

Saakvitne, K., & Pearlman, L. (1996). *Transforming the pain: A workbook on vicarious traumatization.* New York: WW Norton.

Scheeringa, M., & Gaensbauer, T. (2000). Posttraumatic stress disorder. In C. Zeanah, Jr. (Ed), *Handbook of infant mental health,* (2nd ed.), (pp 369–379). New York: Guilford.

Winnicott, D. W. (2002). *Winnicott on the child.* Cambridge, MA: Perseus Books.

National Organizations and Internet Resources

ZERO TO THREE: National Center for Infants, Toddlers and Families;
2000 M Street, NW, Suite 200, Washington, DC 20036. 1 (202) 638-1144;
www.zerotothree.org

ZERO TO THREE is a national organization dedicated to promoting the healthy development of infants and toddlers by strengthening families, communities, and professionals who care for them. The Web site offers handouts and tip sheets for parents and professionals that cover a range of child development issues.

National Organization for the Education of Young Children (NAEYC), 1509 16th Street, NW, Washington, DC 20036. 1(202) 232-8777; www.naeyc.org

NAEYC is an early childhood professional organization that promotes excellence in early childhood education. NAEYC offers high quality resources for parents and professionals, including a monthly magazine full of great information.

Child Care Information Exchange
P.O. Box 3249, Redmond, WA 98073. (800) 221-2864; www.ChildCareExchange.com

The Child Care Exchange offers a wealth of information on child care issues that include research reviews, curriculum ideas and behavior management strategies.

National Child Traumatic Stress Network:
The National Center for Child Traumatic Stress

University of California, Los Angeles, 11159 W. Olympic Blvd, Suite 650, Los Angeles, CA 90064. (310) 235 2633; www.nctsnet.org
A national consortium of organizations formed to raise standards of care and better access to services for children and families exposed to trauma.

National Clearinghouse on Child Abuse and Neglect Information
330 C Street, SW, Washington, DC, 20447. (800) 394-3366; http://nccanch.acf.hhs.gov

The mission of the Clearinghouse is to connect professionals and concerned citizens to practical information on resources that promote the safety and well-being of children and families. The Web site offers free handouts and information guides on issues related to child abuse and neglect.

FEMA for Kids—Federal Emergency Management Agency
www.fema.gov/kids/

A Web site from the Federal Emergency Management Agency, the agency in charge of responding to natural disasters. The FEMA for Kids Web page offers information to parents, teachers, and children on coping with natural disasters.

National Center for Children Exposed to Violence
Yale Child Study Center, 230 South Frontage Road, P.O. Box 207900, New Haven, CT
06520. 1 (203) 785 7047; www.nccev.org

The mission of the NCCEV is to increase the capacity of individuals and communities
to reduce the incidence and impact of violence on children and families, to train professionals and to increase public awareness. The Web site includes a resource center.

American Library Association
50 East Huron Street, Chicago, Illinois, 60611. (800)545-2433; www.ala.org

A great resource for information on high quality children's books. The ALA offers
booklists and guidelines on sharing books about sensitive issues with children
of all ages.

Professional Publications

Quick Reads

From the National Association for the Education of Young Children (NAEYC):
1 (202) 232-8777; www.naeyc.org

- *When Disaster Strikes—A Guide for Early Childhood Professionals*
  (J. Farish, 2003)

  Information and tips on working with young children exposed to catastrophic
  events.

- *Media Violence and Children: A Guide for Parents* (1998)

  A brochure for parents and teachers on the impact of TV and video game violence
  on children.

- *What Happened to the World? Helping Children Cope in Turbulent Times* (J. Green-
  man, 2001)

  Tips for adults to help children who are anxious, fearful, and grieving as a result of
  catastrophic events.

- *Helping Children Learn Self-Control: A Guide to Discipline* (1998)

  Tips for parents and teachers on helping children develop self-discipline and internal controls for their behavior.

Understanding the Effects of Maltreatment on Early Brain Development (National
Clearinghouse on Child Abuse and Neglect Information, October 2001)

An informative and easy-to-read guide about trauma's impact on brain
development.

A Hands-On Approach to Understanding the Brain (P. Walsh, November 2000; in Educational Leadership, 58(3), 76–78)

A very interesting way of understanding the structure and function of the brain
using the human hand as a model.

Professional Books and Journal Articles

Young Children and Trauma: Intervention and Treatment (J. Osofsky, Ed., 2004, New York: Guilford Press)

This edited volume provides a comprehensive collection of chapters by noted professionals in the field of trauma and young children.

Experiencing Violence in a Developmental Context (S. Marans & A. Adelman, 1997, in J. Osofsky, Ed., Children in a Violent Society (pp. 202–222), New York: Guilford Publications)

A comprehensive look at the effects of violence on children's development.

Children Who See Too Much: Lessons from the Child Witness to Violence Project (B. M. Groves, 2002, Boston: Beacon Press)

This book includes focuses on children who have been affected by violence in their homes or communities. It uses case examples, and has information on interventions by teachers, police officers, and health providers.

Early Violence Prevention: Tools for Teachers of Young Children (D. Arezzo, K. Hendrix, R. Slaby, & W. Roedell; 1995, Washington, DC: NAEYC)

The authors of this book offer effective strategies to help children grow up to be assertive but nonviolent in their approach to solving conflict. Interventions include help for children with aggressive behavior patterns, promoting sharing behavior, and teaching assertiveness skills.

Secure Relationships: Nurturing Infant/Toddler Attachment in Early Care Settings (A. Honig, 2002, Washington, DC: NAEYC)

Important information and tips for caregivers on promoting healthy secure relationships in early care and education settings.

Recommended Books for Young Children

Comforting Rhythms and Routines

Good Night Moon (M. W. Brown, 1947, New York: HarperCollins)

A classic bedtime book. Its soothing, rhythmic text and beautiful pictures draw adults and children together in a warm embrace as they say goodnight to the objects around them.

How Do Dinosaurs Say Goodnight? (J. Yolen & M. Teague (Ill.), 2000, New York: Blue Sky Press/Scholastic)

The struggle at bedtime turns silly as dinosaurs cry, stamp, and moan their way to bed. Children love to repeat the simple text and transform their struggle into a cathartic game.

Cara de Bebe (P. Tildes, 2001, Watertown, MA: Charlesbridge Publishing

Baby faces portray a range of emotions in this simple book.

Separation/Separation Anxiety

The Runaway Bunny (M. W. Brown & C. Hurd (Ill.), 1942, New York: HarperCollins)

A mother bunny assures her little bunny that she will love her no matter where her bunny goes. Another classic tale that can help children understand the push–pull of the parent–child relationship.

Owl Babies (M. Waddell & P. Benson (Ill.), 1992, Cambridge, MA: Candlewick Press)

Three baby owls are afraid that their mother owl won't come back to their hole in the tree. They think of ways to stay calm until she returns. Owl Babies is great poetry and toddlers love it. Some children who have experienced traumatic separation may find this book (and other titles about separation) difficult.

Fears and Anxiety

Wemberly Worried (K. Henkes, 2000, New York: Greenwillow Books/HarperCollins)

Poor Wemberly mouse worries about everything—especially the first day of preschool. Special adults in her life help calm her fears.

Darkness and the Butterfly (A. Grifalconi, 1987, New York: Little Brown & Co)

A young African girl named Osa is afraid of the dark. Preschoolers love hearing how the village wise women helps Osa overcome her fears.

Today I Feel Silly and Other Moods That Make My Day (J. L. Curtis & L. Cornell (Ill.), 1998, New York: Joanna Cotler/HarperCollins)

A fun and engaging book that help preschoolers sort out feelings.

Angry Feelings

The Grouchy Ladybug and *The Mixed Up Chameleon* (E. Carle, 1996 and 1984, New York: HarperCollins)

Eric Carle has an award winning series of books beautifully illustrated and cleverly written for toddlers and preschoolers.

Alexander and the Terrible, Horrible, No Good, Very Bad Day (J. Viorst & R. Cruz (Ill.), 1972, New York: Atheneum/Simon & Schuster)

Everything goes wrong for Alexander one day—even the cat won't sleep with him. Alexander struggles to cope with his mad feelings and imagines moving to Australia. Available in Spanish.

Where the Wild Things Are (M. Sendak, 1988, New York: HarperCollins)

Max is in trouble for being "wild." When he is sent to his room without supper, he imagines a world of monsters where he is "king," and returns to find his supper waiting for him. Preschoolers love to play Max and stomp around in angry protest.

When Sophie Gets Angry—Really, Really Angry (M. Bang, 1999, New York: Blue Sky Press/Scholastic)

A Caldecott Honor book, *When Sophie Gets Angry* is a perfect book for the 2–4-year-old child. Simple rhyming text and colorful pictures give life to the angry feelings all children experience and offers ways to express anger in healthy ways.

Don't Rant and Rave on Wednesdays! The Children's Anger Control Book (A. Moser & D. Melton, 1994, Kansas City, KS: Landmark Editions)

One of a series of good books about feelings by this author, *Don't Rant* takes a light-hearted but helpful approach to managing tough feelings.

Feeling Different, Making Friends

Leo the Late Bloomer (R. Krauss &. J. Aruego (Ill.), New York: HarperCollins)

Everyone is worried about little Leo the tiger. When will he grow? Calm adult tigers assure everyone that Leo is just fine and will grow in his own time.

Josephine the Short-Necked Giraffe (F. Rogers, 1969, Pittsburgh: Family Communications)

Feeling different is hard. Josephine helps children who are feeling alone to begin to feel OK about themselves.

Making Friends (F. Rogers (Mister Rogers' First Experiences Books), 1987, New York: Putnam Publishing)

Fred Rogers wrote some of the best issue-oriented books for children. In *Making Friends,* children learn the sometimes tricky skills needed to make friendships.

Amos and Boris (W. Steig, 1971, New York: Farrar, Straus and Giroux Publishers)

Amos and Boris are two animals with an unlikely friendship that ends up saving them both in the end.

Grief and Loss

The Tenth Good Thing About Barney (J. Viorst & E. Blegvad (Ill.), 1987, London: Aladdin Publishing Company)

A boy struggles with grief when his cat dies. His family helps him understand death and his feelings about it by planning a good-bye for Barney.

So Much to Think About (F. Rogers, 1991, Pittsburgh: Family Communications)

A thoughtful book for young children about losing a loved one.

Nana Upstairs, Nana Downstairs (T. DePaola, 1997, New York: Putnam Press)

Four-year-old Tommy has to say good–bye to his beloved Nana when she dies.

Other Topics

A Chair For My Mother (V. Williams, 1982, New York: Greenwillow Books/Harper-Collins)

A girl and her family struggle to recover from a house fire. With the help of neighbors and family, they triumph. Available in Spanish.

Smoky Night (E. Bunting & D. Diaz (Ill.), 1994, San Diego, CA: Harcourt Children's Books)

A 1995 Caldecott medal winner, *Smoky Night* is about a night of rioting and street violence. Young Daniel's mother explains violent behavior to him and they struggle to make relationships with neighbors from another culture.

I Do and I Don't (F. Rogers, H. Sharapan, & L. Steadman (Ill.), 1993, Pittsburgh: Family Communications)

This book helps children sort out their conflicting and confusing feelings about home when hard things happen there.